# REVISE OCR GCSE (9–1)
## Computer Science

# REVISION WORKBOOK

Series Consultant: Harry Smith

Author: David Waller

- - - - - - - - - - - - - - - - - - - - - - - - - - - - - - - - - - - - - - - - - -

## Also available to support your revision:

The **Revise GCSE Study Skills Guide** is full of tried-and-trusted hints and tips for how to learn more effectively. It gives you techniques to help you achieve your best – throughout your GCSE studies and beyond!

The **Revise GCSE Revision Planner** helps you to plan and organise your time, step-by-step, throughout your GCSE revision. Use this book and wall chart to mastermind your revision.

For the full range of Pearson revision titles across KS2, KS3, GCSE, Functional Skills, AS/A Level and BTEC visit: www.pearsonschools.co.uk/revise

# Contents

### A small bit of small print

OCR publishes Sample Assessment Material and the Specification on its website. This is the official content and this book should be used in conjunction with it. The questions have been written to help you practise every topic in the book. Remember: the real exam questions may not look like this.

**1-to-1** page match with the **Computer Science Revision Guide** ISBN 9781292133904

ii

# The central processing unit

 **1** The table below shows some components of the CPU and their functions.

Complete the table below by filling in the missing information.

| Component of CPU | Function |
|---|---|
| CU (control unit) | |
| Clock | Controls the rate at which program instructions are carried out. |
| ALU (arithmetic logic unit) | |
| Cache | Stores frequently used program instructions and data so the processor isn't kept waiting for them to be transferred from the main memory. |
| Registers | |

**(5 marks)**

 **2** Alva is buying a new laptop.
The sales assistant recommends one with a 3 GHz CPU.
He claims that it will always out-perform one with a 2 GHz CPU.

Explain why this may not be the case.

> You need to explain why the sales assistant would think that a 3 GHz processor will give better performance, but also mention other factors that can affect performance that Alva should consider.

Usually this is the case, but it might not be because your CPU might have less clock speed, but your CPU could have higher clock cache size, which would help as it would store temporary files from past executions to make future requests faster. Another reason less clock speed isn't always worse is threads cores, as with more cores you will have more power to run multiple programs at once.

**(6 marks)**

# Components of the CPU

**1** List **two** components with which the CPU works to execute program instructions.

> The question is asking about other components of the computer, not components of the CPU itself.

1 ~~ALU~~  Memory

2 Input & Output devices

**(2 marks)**

**2** Describe the role of the CU (control unit) and the ALU (arithmetic logic unit) in the fetch–decode–execute cycle.

> This question is asking you to 'describe' and not just state the functions of the components. You must make at least two points about each one.

CU

In the F-D-E cycle the C U decodes the instructions

ALU

In the F-D-E cycle the ALU executes all the programs

**(4 marks)**

**3** Within the CPU, there are memory locations called registers. Some of these perform specific functions during the fetch–decode–execute cycle.

> You are asked to 'state' and as there is 1 mark for each answer you only need to make one correct point. The first answer has been done for you.

State the function of the following registers.

Program counter

**Guided**

This holds the address of the next instruction to be fetched.

MDR (memory data register)

Holds the content found at the address held in the MAR

Accumulator

It is the register used to hold the results of the ALU

**(3 marks)**

# Fetch–decode–execute cycle 1

**1** The design of the 'stored program computer' and the way in which it works is known as 'von Neumann architecture'.

> See page 2 of the Revision Guide for a reminder on von Neumann architecture.

(a) State **two** components of von Neumann's design in addition to the CPU.

1 ...............................................................................................................................

...............................................................................................................................

2 ...............................................................................................................................

............................................................................................................... **(2 marks)**

(b) Define the term 'stored program computer'.

...............................................................................................................................

............................................................................................................... **(1 mark)**

**2** The von Neumann architecture carries out computer programs using the fetch–decode–execute cycle.

(a) The table below describes stages in the fetch–decode–execute cycle but they are not in order.
Write the numbers 1–4 in the empty cells to show the correct order.

| Description | Order |
|---|---|
| The next instruction is sent from the RAM to the CPU. | |
| The instruction is carried out. | |
| The CU interprets the instruction. | |
| The CPU sends a signal to the RAM requesting the next instruction. | |

**(2 marks)**

(b) State the role of RAM in the fetch–decode–execute cycle.

...............................................................................................................................

............................................................................................................... **(1 mark)**

(c) Annotate the diagram to show the role of the CU and ALU in the fetch–decode–execute cycle. **(2 marks)**

| **CU (control unit)** | **ALU (arithmetic logic unit)** |
|---|---|
| The CU _____ the instructions. If a calculation is needed, the CU instructs the _____. | _____ are carried out in the ALU. |

# Fetch–decode–execute cycle 2

1   The fetch–decode–execute cycle makes use of registers.
Describe what is meant by a register.

> The question says 'describe' and there are 2 marks so you must give a detailed account.
> You could say what they are used for AND why they are useful.

.................................................................................................................................

................................................................................................................................. **(2 marks)**

2   The table below shows instructions and data stored in the main memory of a computer.

| Address | Contents |
|---------|----------|
| 0 | LOAD 3 |
| 1 | ADD 4 |
| 2 | STORE 5 |
| 3 | 9 |
| 4 | 3 |
| 5 | |

Table 1 shows the contents of the registers at the end of the first fetch–decode–execute cycle.

Table 1

| Program Counter | 1 |
|-----------------|---|
| MAR | 0 |
| MDR | LOAD 3 |
| Accumulator | 9 |

(a)   Complete Table 2 to show the contents of the registers at the end of the second cycle.   **(4 marks)**

Table 2

| Program Counter | |
|-----------------|---|
| MAR | |
| MDR | |
| Accumulator | |

(b)   Complete Table 3 to show the contents of the registers at the end of the third cycle.   **(4 marks)**

Table 3

| Program Counter | |
|-----------------|---|
| MAR | |
| MDR | |
| Accumulator | |

(c)   Explain the actions that are carried out by this program.

.................................................................................................................................

.................................................................................................................................

.................................................................................................................................

................................................................................................................................. **(2 marks)**

# Performance of the CPU

**1** Explain why cache memory is used in the CPU.

> You have been asked to 'explain', so you must give a detailed answer.

........................................................................................................................................

........................................................................................................................................

........................................................................................................................................

........................................................................................................................................ **(2 marks)**

**2** The diagram shows a particular type of processor.

| Control unit | | Control unit | |
|---|---|---|---|
| Arithmetic and logic unit | | Arithmetic and logic unit | |
| | Core 0 | | Core 1 |

(a) State the type of processor shown in the diagram.

........................................................................................................................................

........................................................................................................................................ **(1 mark)**

(b) Explain why processors of this type can improve performance.

........................................................................................................................................

........................................................................................................................................

........................................................................................................................................

........................................................................................................................................ **(2 marks)**

(c) The performance of a CPU can be improved by increasing its clock speed. Explain why performance cannot be increased indefinitely by increasing the clock speed.

........................................................................................................................................

........................................................................................................................................

........................................................................................................................................

........................................................................................................................................ **(2 marks)**

**3** Give **one** reason why cache memory is not used for RAM.

........................................................................................................................................

........................................................................................................................................ **(1 mark)**

**4** Explain why sequential programs might not run quicker with multi-core processors.

........................................................................................................................................

........................................................................................................................................ **(2 marks)**

# Embedded systems

**1** (a) Elaine has been told that her digital camera is controlled by an embedded system. Define what is meant by an 'embedded system'.

.................................................................................................................................

................................................................................................................. **(1 mark)**

(b) Identify **three** components of an embedded system.

> You have been asked to 'identify' components. There are more possibilities than you have been asked for.

1 ...............................................................................................................

2 ...............................................................................................................

3 ............................................................................................................... **(3 marks)**

(c) List **two** other devices that contain embedded systems.

.................................................................................................................................

................................................................................................................. **(2 marks)**

**2** Desktop computers are referred to as 'general purpose machines' and embedded systems are called 'special purpose machines'.

(a) Explain the difference between these two types of system.

.................................................................................................................................

.................................................................................................................................

.................................................................................................................................

................................................................................................................. **(2 marks)**

(b) Explain why embedded systems are also referred to as 'real-time' systems.

.................................................................................................................................

.................................................................................................................................

.................................................................................................................................

................................................................................................................. **(2 marks)**

(c) Explain why low-level languages such as assembly language are used for writing the programs for embedded systems.

> For a reminder on assembly language, look at page 69 of the Revision Guide.

.................................................................................................................................

.................................................................................................................................

.................................................................................................................................

................................................................................................................. **(2 marks)**

# RAM and ROM

**1** The main memory of a computer consists of both volatile and non-volatile memory.

   (a) Define what is meant by 'volatile memory'.

.................................................................................................................................

................................................................................................................. **(1 mark)**

   (b) State what non-volatile main memory is used for.

.................................................................................................................................

................................................................................................................. **(1 mark)**

**2** Complete this table by placing a tick in the column next to the true statements.

| Statement | True |
|---|---|
| RAM stands for Random Access Memory | |
| ROM is volatile | |
| Data can be read from and written to ROM | |
| Program instructions and data are stored in RAM | |
| The sets of instructions needed for a computer to start are stored in ROM | |

**(5 marks)**

**3** A computer's main memory consists of both RAM and ROM.
Compare RAM and ROM.

> You have been asked to 'compare' RAM and ROM. This means that you have to give an account of the differences between them. Remember to refer to **both** of them for each difference or similarity. There are three marks for this question, so your answer should have three differences or similarities.

.................................................................................................................................

.................................................................................................................................

.................................................................................................................................

.................................................................................................................................

.................................................................................................................................

................................................................................................................. **(3 marks)**

**4** State **one** example of data which is stored in RAM.

.................................................................................................................................

................................................................................................................. **(1 mark)**

# Virtual memory

1   Computers sometimes make use of virtual memory.

    (a)   Explain what is meant by 'virtual memory'.

> You have been asked to 'explain'. This means that you must give a detailed account of virtual memory giving the important facts, e.g. what it is used for, why it is needed and where it is found.

......................................................................................................................

......................................................................................................................

......................................................................................................................

......................................................................................................................

**(3 marks)**

    (b)   Explain why a computer sometimes needs to make use of virtual memory.

......................................................................................................................

......................................................................................................................

......................................................................................................................   **(2 marks)**

    (c)   Explain how a computer's operating system manages the use of the virtual memory.

......................................................................................................................

......................................................................................................................

......................................................................................................................

......................................................................................................................

......................................................................................................................

......................................................................................................................   **(4 marks)**

2   John's computer is using virtual memory.

    (a)   Explain how the use of virtual memory affects the performance of the computer.

> Remember that there are both benefits and drawbacks when using virtual memory.

......................................................................................................................

......................................................................................................................

......................................................................................................................   **(2 marks)**

    (b)   Explain **one** action that John could take to prevent the need for using virtual memory.

......................................................................................................................

......................................................................................................................

......................................................................................................................   **(2 marks)**

# Secondary storage 1: optical and magnetic devices

1   Most computer systems use at least one secondary storage device.

(a)   Give **two** reasons why a secondary storage device is needed in most computer systems.

1 ........................................................................................................................................

........................................................................................................................................

2 ........................................................................................................................................

........................................................................................................................................ **(2 marks)**

(b)   Some secondary storage devices are magnetic and some are optical.

> These questions ask you to 'describe' how data is stored on magnetic and optical drives. You will not gain the marks by just stating that the data is stored 'by magnetism' or 'by laser'; you will need to describe the structure of the devices and explain how the data is written and read.

(i)   Describe how data is stored on magnetic storage devices.

........................................................................................................................................

........................................................................................................................................

........................................................................................................................................

........................................................................................................................................ **(2 marks)**

(ii)   Describe how data is stored on optical storage devices.

........................................................................................................................................

........................................................................................................................................

........................................................................................................................................

........................................................................................................................................ **(2 marks)**

(c)   Explain why magnetic devices are used in preference to optical ones as the main storage devices in most computer systems.

> This question is worth 2 marks so your answer should include two different points.

........................................................................................................................................

........................................................................................................................................

........................................................................................................................................

........................................................................................................................................ **(2 marks)**

2   Noah has 200 photos that he wants to put on a CD or DVD. Each photo is 8 MB in size. Calculate whether all his photos can be saved on a single CD or on a single DVD.

........................................................................................................................................

........................................................................................................................................

........................................................................................................................................

........................................................................................................................................ **(2 marks)**

# Secondary storage 2: solid-state memory

1  Serena has bought a 6 GB SD card for use as secondary storage.

(a)  Calculate how many megabytes there are in 6 GB.

> For a reminder on calculating with bytes, see page 72 of the Revision Guide. Make sure that you always show all your working when carrying out calculations.

.................................................................................................................................

.................................................................................................................................

.................................................................................................................................

................................................................................................................................. **(1 mark)**

(b)  An SD card is an example of a solid-state storage device.

(i)  Give a reason why it is called a 'solid-state' storage device.

.................................................................................................................................

................................................................................................................................. **(1 mark)**

(ii)  Apart from SD cards, state **two** other uses of solid-state storage.

1 ..............................................................................................................................

.................................................................................................................................

2 ..............................................................................................................................

................................................................................................................................. **(2 marks)**

(iii)  Gloria has removed the hard disk drive from her laptop and replaced it with a solid-state drive.
Give **two** reasons why this is a suitable upgrade.

.................................................................................................................................

.................................................................................................................................

.................................................................................................................................

................................................................................................................................. **(2 marks)**

(c)  Describe how data is stored on a solid-state drive.

> As this is a 'describe' question, you will need to stress that the data is stored using transistors that retain their state when the power is turned off.

.................................................................................................................................

.................................................................................................................................

.................................................................................................................................

................................................................................................................................. **(2 marks)**

# Storage 3: capacity, speed and cost

1　Compare the characteristics of magnetic and solid-state secondary storage.

> You need to compare the characteristics mentioned in the specification – capacity, speed, portability, durability, reliability and cost. Some of these are on page 12 of the Revision Guide. You might find it helpful to add headings to your answer to remind yourself of the different characteristics as you are writing your response.
>
> The first part of the answer about capacity has been done for you.

**Guided**

Capacity

At the present time, magnetic storage devices have the highest capacity,

commonly 1 to 2 TB in home computers. Solid-state drives are becoming larger

and laptops often have drives of 500 GB to 1 TB.

.......................................................................................................

.......................................................................................................

.......................................................................................................

.......................................................................................................

.......................................................................................................

.......................................................................................................

.......................................................................................................

.......................................................................................................

.......................................................................................................

.......................................................................................................

.......................................................................................................

.......................................................................................................

.......................................................................................................

.......................................................................................................

.......................................................................................................

.......................................................................................................

.......................................................................................................

.......................................................................................................

.......................................................................................................

....................................................................................... **(8 marks)**

# Storage 4: portability, durability and reliability

**1** Ollie has bought a small laptop computer.

(a) There are three types of secondary storage device: magnetic, optical and solid-state.

> To answer this question, you may need to look back at page 11 of the Revision Guide.

   (i) State which type of storage is most suitable for a small laptop computer.

.........................................................................................................................................

**(1 mark)**

   (ii) Explain why this type of storage is the most suitable for this type of computer.

> You have been asked to 'explain', so detailed answers are required. Use the number of marks for the question as a guide.

.........................................................................................................................................

.........................................................................................................................................

.........................................................................................................................................

.........................................................................................................................................

.........................................................................................................................................

.........................................................................................................................................

**(4 marks)**

(b) Ollie gets a free DVD containing images and programs attached to a computer magazine.
Give **two** reasons why a DVD is suitable for this purpose.

1 .......................................................................................................................................

.........................................................................................................................................

2 .......................................................................................................................................

.........................................................................................................................................

**(2 marks)**

(c) State whether a DVD is magnetic, optical or solid-state storage.

.........................................................................................................................................

**(1 mark)**

(d) Ollie's desktop computer has both a magnetic hard disk drive and a solid-state drive. Explain why a desktop computer would have both instead of just having a solid-state drive.

> You need to think about the characteristics of the two storage methods and give situations when each would be useful.

.........................................................................................................................................

.........................................................................................................................................

.........................................................................................................................................

.........................................................................................................................................

.........................................................................................................................................

.........................................................................................................................................

**(4 marks)**

# Networks 1: LANs and WANs

1  A small business has six standalone computers, a printer and an internet connection in an office. The office manager is thinking of linking the computers to form a network.

(a) Describe what is meant by a network.

..................................................................................................................................

..................................................................................................................................

..................................................................................................................................

..................................................................................................................... **(2 marks)**

(b) State **two** advantages of connecting the computers to form a network.

1 ...............................................................................................................................

..................................................................................................................................

2 ...............................................................................................................................

..................................................................................................................... **(2 marks)**

2  Two types of network are a LAN (local area network) and a WAN (wide area network). Describe the characteristics of a LAN and a WAN.

> You are being asked to 'describe' the characteristics of a LAN and a WAN so don't just state what each one is. You must describe some of the features of each one. Use the number of marks as a guide for the number of points you need to make.

LAN

..................................................................................................................................

..................................................................................................................................

..................................................................................................................................

..................................................................................................................................

..................................................................................................................................

WAN

..................................................................................................................................

..................................................................................................................................

..................................................................................................................................

..................................................................................................................................

..................................................................................................................... **(6 marks)**

# Networks 2: client–server and peer-to-peer

1   A computer consultant, giving advice on office networks, suggested that a small company with only six computers should install a peer-to-peer network but suggested that a large company with over one hundred computers should install a client–server network.

(a)   Describe the characteristics of a 'peer-to-peer' network.

........................................................................................................................

........................................................................................................................

........................................................................................................................

........................................................................................................................

........................................................................................................................

........................................................................................................................   **(3 marks)**

(b)   Explain **two** benefits to the small company of installing a peer-to-peer network rather than a client–server one.

> You are **not** being asked about the benefits of using a network but about the benefits to a small company of installing a peer-to-peer network rather than a client–server network.

1   ....................................................................................................................

........................................................................................................................

........................................................................................................................

........................................................................................................................

2   ....................................................................................................................

........................................................................................................................

........................................................................................................................

........................................................................................................................   **(4 marks)**

(c)   The consultant advised the large company to install a client–server network. Give **two** reasons why the consultant might have given this advice.

1   ....................................................................................................................

........................................................................................................................

........................................................................................................................

........................................................................................................................

2   ....................................................................................................................

........................................................................................................................

........................................................................................................................

........................................................................................................................   **(4 marks)**

# Transmission media

1   Devices on a network communicate using copper wired cable or fibre optic cable.

> When you compare two items you must specifically refer to them by name in the answer.

    (a)   Compare the method of data transmission in the two types of cable.

......................................................................................................................

......................................................................................................................

.................................................................................................................. **(2 marks)**

    (b)   State **one** advantage and **one** disadvantage of using fibre optic cable rather than copper cable.

Advantage

......................................................................................................................

Disadvantage

.................................................................................................................. **(2 marks)**

2   Network data can be transmitted over wireless networks using radio waves.

    (a)   State the range of frequencies commonly used for data transmission in wireless networks.

.................................................................................................................. **(1 mark)**

    (b)   A network device is advertised as transmitting on channel 6.
        Explain what is meant by a channel.

......................................................................................................................

......................................................................................................................

.................................................................................................................. **(2 marks)**

3   Compare the use of cable or wireless as the transmission medium by considering:

    (a)   Security

......................................................................................................................

......................................................................................................................

    (b)   Interference

......................................................................................................................

......................................................................................................................

    (c)   Bandwidth

......................................................................................................................

.................................................................................................................. **(6 marks)**

# Connecting computers to a LAN

On this page, there are lots of 'describe' and 'explain' questions with 2 or 4 marks. These questions require you to make several points in the answer. The first one has been done for you as an example.

**1** (a)  Describe the role of NICs (network interface controllers) in connecting devices to computer networks.

> There are 2 marks for this question and two points have been made in the description.

**Guided**

A NIC provides a physical connection to either a wired or a wireless network for

a device on the network. The NIC formats the data so that it can be transmitted

and received across the network.

**(2 marks)**

(b)  Explain how each NIC is uniquely identified and addressed on the network.

.............................................................................................................................

.............................................................................................................................

.............................................................................................................................

**(2 marks)**

**2**  Devices on a network can be linked using switches.
Explain why using a switch to connect devices on a network is preferable to using a hub.

.............................................................................................................................

.............................................................................................................................

.............................................................................................................................

.............................................................................................................................

**(3 marks)**

**3**  When Anika takes her laptop to school, she can connect it without using a cable to the school's cable network.

(a)  State the role of a wireless access point in a network.

.............................................................................................................................

**(1 mark)**

(b)  Anika's family has a home network.
Explain the role of the router in Anika's home network.

> There are 4 marks for this question, so you cannot just say 'it connects networks together'. You must name the networks that are being connected and explain how the router ensures that all members of the household receive the correct data.

.............................................................................................................................

.............................................................................................................................

.............................................................................................................................

.............................................................................................................................

.............................................................................................................................

**(4 marks)**

# The internet

1  (a)  Ayana is using her computer to access the internet and has used a program to find out her IP address. The program informs her that it is 213.36.27.127.

    (i)  Explain why a computer requires an IP address to access the internet.

..............................................................................................................................

..............................................................................................................................

..............................................................................................................................

.............................................................................................................................. **(2 marks)**

    (ii)  An IP address consists of four numbers, each between 0 and 255.
State how many bits will be needed to store the IP address.

.............................................................................................................................. **(1 mark)**

  (b)  When Ayana accesses websites, she types in a name such as www.ocr.org.uk instead of the IP address.
Explain how Ayana is able to access the website using the domain name rather than the IP address.

..............................................................................................................................

..............................................................................................................................

..............................................................................................................................

.............................................................................................................................. **(2 marks)**

2  Ayana would like to use her computer as a web host on the internet.

  (a)  State what is meant by a web host.

..............................................................................................................................

.............................................................................................................................. **(1 mark)**

  (b)  Identify **four** changes to her normal computer and internet use that Ayana will encounter if she uses her computer as a web host on the internet.

> For this question, you will have to apply your knowledge and think about the implications of hosting a website on your own computer rather than using a hosting company. The most obvious one has been done for you.

**Guided**

1 Ayana will have to keep her computer switched on 24 hours a day, 7 days a week.
..............................................................................................................................

..............................................................................................................................

2 ...........................................................................................................................

..............................................................................................................................

3 ...........................................................................................................................

..............................................................................................................................

4 ...........................................................................................................................

.............................................................................................................................. **(4 marks)**

# Network topologies

1   A small business is going to connect its standalone computers together using a star topology.

(a)   With the aid of a diagram, describe a star topology.

> You need to draw an annotated diagram with descriptions of the components.

**(2 marks)**

(b)   Give **three** reasons why the business would choose to use a star topology.

1 ..................................................................................................................................

..................................................................................................................................

..................................................................................................................................

..................................................................................................................................

2 ..................................................................................................................................

..................................................................................................................................

..................................................................................................................................

3 ..................................................................................................................................

..................................................................................................................................

..................................................................................................................................

..................................................................................................... **(3 marks)**

# Protocols 1: browsers and email clients

1 When computers on a network communicate with each other they need to use the same protocols.

(a) Describe **three** functions of protocols in controlling how data is sent across networks.

1 ...........................................................................................................................................

...........................................................................................................................................

2 ...........................................................................................................................................

...........................................................................................................................................

3 ...........................................................................................................................................

........................................................................................................................................... **(6 marks)**

(b) This table lists some of the protocols used by computers when communicating over the internet.
Complete the table by inserting the protocol next to its function. The first one has been done for you.

| Protocol | Function |
|----------|----------|
| HTTPS | Used when communications between a client and host have to be encrypted. |
| | Provides the rules for sending email messages from client to server and then from server to server until they reach their destination. |
| | Provides the rules to be followed by web browsers when accessing the internet and by web servers when requesting and supplying information. |
| | Provides the rules for transferring files between computers. |

**(3 marks)**

(c) Two protocols used in networks are TCP and IP.

(i) State what the initials TCP and IP stand for.

...........................................................................................................................................

........................................................................................................................................... **(1 mark)**

(ii) Describe the functions of these two protocols.

TCP

...........................................................................................................................................

...........................................................................................................................................

...........................................................................................................................................

IP

...........................................................................................................................................

...........................................................................................................................................

........................................................................................................................................... **(4 marks)**

Had a go ☐  Nearly there ☐  Nailed it! ☐

# Protocols 2: network layers

1  TCP/IP is a protocol stack used in networking. There are four layers in the stack.

(a)  State the purposes of the following layers.

> The question asks you to state the purposes, so you do not need to give a detailed explanation. Use the total number of marks as a guide for how much you need to write.

Application layer

........................................................................................................................

........................................................................................................................

Transport layer

........................................................................................................................

........................................................................................................................

Network access layer

........................................................................................................................

........................................................................................................................ **(3 marks)**

(b)  Identify a protocol associated with each of the following layers.

Application layer

........................................................................................................................

Transport layer

........................................................................................................................

Internet layer

........................................................................................................................ **(3 marks)**

2  TCP/IP is a set of protocols (protocol stack) based on layers.
List the four layers of the protocol stack, in order.

1 ......................................................................................................................

2 ......................................................................................................................

3 ......................................................................................................................

4 ...................................................................................................................... **(4 marks)**

# Protocols 3: benefits of layers

1   Explain **three** benefits of having the protocols arranged in layers.

1 ......................................................................................................................................

......................................................................................................................................

2 ......................................................................................................................................

......................................................................................................................................

3 ......................................................................................................................................

...................................................................................................... **(6 marks)**

2   David is working abroad for his company and, while he is away, he communicates with his colleagues using a virtual network.

(a)  Describe what is meant by a 'virtual network'.

......................................................................................................................................

......................................................................................................................................

......................................................................................................................................

...................................................................................................... **(2 marks)**

(b)  Describe **two** benefits to David and his colleagues of using virtual networks.

1 ......................................................................................................................................

......................................................................................................................................

......................................................................................................................................

......................................................................................................................................

2 ......................................................................................................................................

......................................................................................................................................

......................................................................................................................................

...................................................................................................... **(4 marks)**

3   Explain how protocols help manufacturers and developers of hardware and software.

......................................................................................................................................

......................................................................................................................................

......................................................................................................................................

...................................................................................................... **(2 marks)**

# Packets and packet switching

These questions mainly use 'state' and require a single point without a full explanation or description.

**1** When data is transferred between computers across a network, it is broken down into small packets.

(a) State why data is broken down into packets for transmission across a network.

..............................................................................................................................................

.................................................................................................................... **(1 mark)**

(b) The packets are transmitted across the network by a process called packet switching.

(i) Describe the transmission of the packets across a network using packet switching.

..............................................................................................................................

..............................................................................................................................

..............................................................................................................................

..............................................................................................................................

.......................................................................................................... **(4 marks)**

(ii) State **one** benefit of using packet switching.

..............................................................................................................................

.......................................................................................................... **(1 mark)**

**2** A large company has decided to store its data in the cloud.
State **two** advantages and **two** disadvantages for the company of storing its data in the cloud.

The question is not asking you to explain what is meant by 'cloud storage' but to say how it could be useful for the company and state any problems it could cause.

Advantages

1 ...........................................................................................................................

..............................................................................................................................

2 ...........................................................................................................................

..............................................................................................................................

Disadvantages

1 ...........................................................................................................................

..............................................................................................................................

2 ...........................................................................................................................

.......................................................................................................... **(4 marks)**

# Threats to networks 1: people as the weak point

1  'Users pose the greatest threat to the security of networks.'
Discuss how network and password policies can reduce the security threats posed by users.

> You should explain how users can directly harm networks by their actions or allow access to criminals by their lack of security awareness and training.
>
> The answer should have a short introduction and a conclusion.

..................................................................................................................................................

..................................................................................................................................................

..................................................................................................................................................

..................................................................................................................................................

..................................................................................................................................................

..................................................................................................................................................

..................................................................................................................................................

..................................................................................................................................................

..................................................................................................................................................

..................................................................................................................................................

..................................................................................................................................................

..................................................................................................................................................

..................................................................................................................................................

..................................................................................................................................................

..................................................................................................................................................

..................................................................................................................................................

..................................................................................................................................................

..................................................................................................................................................

..................................................................................................................................................

..................................................................................................................................................

..................................................................................................................................................

..................................................................................................................................................

..................................................................................................................................................

..................................................................................................................................................

..................................................................................................................................................

..................................................................................................................................................

.................................................................................................................................. **(8 marks)**

# Threats to networks 2: malware

1  Computer viruses, Trojans, worms and spyware are all types of malware.
Describe the ways in which these types of malware are spread and how they disrupt
the functions of a computer or computer system.

> You are asked to describe the characteristics of four different types of malware. Use
> headings in your answer to remind you to describe each type of malware. Use the number
> of marks as a guide to how much you should write.

Virus

......................................................................................................................................

......................................................................................................................................

......................................................................................................................................

......................................................................................................................................

Trojan

......................................................................................................................................

......................................................................................................................................

......................................................................................................................................

......................................................................................................................................

Worm

......................................................................................................................................

......................................................................................................................................

......................................................................................................................................

......................................................................................................................................

Spyware

......................................................................................................................................

......................................................................................................................................

......................................................................................................................................

......................................................................................................................... **(8 marks)**

2  State **four** defensive measures that can be taken against malware.

......................................................................................................................................

......................................................................................................................................

......................................................................................................................................

......................................................................................................................... **(4 marks)**

# Threats to networks 3: network security

1  Many attacks on networks target vulnerabilities in network operating systems.

> These questions are asking you to 'explain' and 'describe'. There are 2 marks for each answer and you must make more than one point. You should give a general definition and then more details about the forms of attack.

(a)  Explain what is meant by a 'brute force' attack.

..........................................................................................................................

..........................................................................................................................

.......................................................................................................... **(2 marks)**

(b)  Describe the following methods of attacking networks.

SQL injection

> You should describe why SQL is used and how it can pose a security threat to networks.

..........................................................................................................................

..........................................................................................................................

..........................................................................................................................

Denial of service (DoS)

> You should state what service is being denied, how this causes problems and how hackers make it happen.

..........................................................................................................................

..........................................................................................................................

..........................................................................................................................

Data interception and theft

> You should explain how data transmitted on networks can be read and why this is a security risk.

..........................................................................................................................

..........................................................................................................................

.......................................................................................................... **(6 marks)**

2  Give **two** reasons why criminals or hacktivists might use a DoS attack on a company website.

..........................................................................................................................

..........................................................................................................................

.......................................................................................................... **(2 marks)**

# Identifying and preventing vulnerabilities 1

1  Jamail has started work at a new company and has been asked to read and sign the network policies.

> Network policies are designed to ensure that employees do not endanger the security of the network. All your answers should reflect this.

(a)  One of these policies prohibits Jamail from using his own removable media devices on the network.

    (i)  State **two** removable media devices that would be covered by the policy.

    1 ................................................................................................................

    2 ................................................................................................................ **(2 marks)**

    (ii)  State **two** ways in which the use of a removable media device by an employee could be a security threat.

    1 ................................................................................................................

    ................................................................................................................

    2 ................................................................................................................

................................................................................................................ **(2 marks)**

(b)  Another of the network policies concerns rules for the creation and use of passwords.
State **three** rules for passwords that the company should ensure that all employees adhere to.

> You should state three **different** rules – they should not all be about the number and types of characters.

1 ................................................................................................................

................................................................................................................

2 ................................................................................................................

................................................................................................................

3 ................................................................................................................

................................................................................................................ **(3 marks)**

(c)  The company has asked a team of consultants to assess its network security.

    (i)  Explain the role of penetration testing in assessing network security.

    ................................................................................................................

    ................................................................................................................ **(2 marks)**

    (ii)  The consultants suggest that the company implements a policy of user access control.
    Explain how controlling user access levels helps to improve network security.

    ................................................................................................................

    ................................................................................................................ **(2 marks)**

# Identifying and preventing vulnerabilities 2

**1** An organisation has set up a WAN linking its offices and factories throughout the country.

Explain **three** system measures that the organisation will need to take to ensure the security of its network.

> The question asks about system measures, so your answer must be about the computer network, and not about users' actions.
>
> Your answer should include precautions provided by software and hardware. You are asked to 'explain', so you need to give more detail than simply stating the methods.
>
> Use the number of marks as a guide to the amount you need to write.
>
> Your answer should **not** include network policies such as password rules or connecting personal devices.

1 ........................................................................................................................................

...........................................................................................................................................

...........................................................................................................................................

...........................................................................................................................................

2 ........................................................................................................................................

...........................................................................................................................................

...........................................................................................................................................

...........................................................................................................................................

3 ........................................................................................................................................

...........................................................................................................................................

...........................................................................................................................................

................................................................................................................... **(6 marks)**

**2** Give **one** reason why it is important for an organisation to ensure that the operating systems on its computers are kept up to date.

...........................................................................................................................................

...........................................................................................................................................

...........................................................................................................................................

................................................................................................................... **(2 marks)**

Had a go ☐   Nearly there ☐   Nailed it! ☐

# Operating systems 1

1   Describe the role of systems software in a computer system.

You are expected to give a general overview of 'systems software'.

...........................................................................................................................

...........................................................................................................................

...........................................................................................................................

........................................................................................................... **(2 marks)**

2   (a)   Explain the role of the operating system in memory management and multitasking.

Use the number of marks as a guide to how much to write. Part (a) is worth 4 marks, and parts (b) and (c) are worth 2 marks each, so your answer to part (a) should be longer than your answers to parts (b) and (c).

...........................................................................................................................

...........................................................................................................................

...........................................................................................................................

...........................................................................................................................

...........................................................................................................................

...........................................................................................................................

...........................................................................................................................

........................................................................................................... **(4 marks)**

(b)   Explain why file management is used.

...........................................................................................................................

...........................................................................................................................

...........................................................................................................................

........................................................................................................... **(2 marks)**

(c)   Explain how file permissions are used on shared computer systems or on a network.

...........................................................................................................................

...........................................................................................................................

...........................................................................................................................

........................................................................................................... **(2 marks)**

# Operating systems 2

**1** Two of the functions of the operating system are to manage the computer users and provide an interface between them and the hardware and software of the computer system.

Outline how the operating system carries out these two functions.

> The question is asking you to outline two functions – 'manage' computer users and provide an 'interface'. Even though these functions are linked, you must comment on both.
>
> In your answer, you should avoid simply rewriting information already given in the question. This will save you time in the exam. For example, you would not get a mark for writing 'On shared computers, the operating system manages users.'
>
> Make sure you read the question properly and only write relevant information.

Managing computer users

.....................................................................................................................

.....................................................................................................................

.....................................................................................................................

.....................................................................................................................

.....................................................................................................................

.....................................................................................................................

Providing an interface

.....................................................................................................................

.....................................................................................................................

.....................................................................................................................

.....................................................................................................................

.....................................................................................................................

..................................................................................................... **(6 marks)**

**2** Peripheral devices are used to input data and output information into and out of a computer system.

Explain how the operating system manages peripheral devices.

.....................................................................................................................

.....................................................................................................................

.....................................................................................................................

..................................................................................................... **(2 marks)**

# Utility system software

**1** Stephen's computer is running slowly and he thinks it's because his hard disk drive is fragmented.

(a) State what is meant by 'fragmented'.

.................................................................................................................................

................................................................................................................. **(1 mark)**

(b) Explain how defragmentation software will help to make the computer run more quickly.

.................................................................................................................................

.................................................................................................................................

.................................................................................................................................

................................................................................................................. **(2 marks)**

(c) Stephen is advised to use data compression software to create more space on his hard disk drive.

  (i) Give another instance when Stephen should use compression software.

.................................................................................................................................

................................................................................................................. **(1 mark)**

  (ii) Describe the difference between lossless and lossy compression.

.................................................................................................................................

.................................................................................................................................

.................................................................................................................................

................................................................................................................. **(2 marks)**

(d) Stephen wants to make copies of all of his programs and files using backup software. The software allows Stephen to make a full backup whenever he wants.

  (i) State the name of a different backup strategy that Stephen could use.

................................................................................................................. **(1 mark)**

  (ii) Explain how this method should reduce the time spent on backing up.

.................................................................................................................................

.................................................................................................................................

.................................................................................................................................

................................................................................................................. **(2 marks)**

**2** Explain why encryption software is used.

.................................................................................................................................

.................................................................................................................................

.................................................................................................................................

................................................................................................................. **(2 marks)**

# Ethical and legal issues

1   Discuss the legal and ethical implications of the following situations.

> The question asks you to 'discuss'. This means that you have to give a considered and balanced review that includes a range of ideas.

(a)   Users continually changing their devices such as smartphones, tablets and computers.

> You may need to look at pages 32–34 of the Revision Guide for information to answer this question.

.......................................................................................................................................

.......................................................................................................................................

.......................................................................................................................................

.......................................................................................................................................

.......................................................................................................................................

.......................................................................................................................................

....................................................................................................................... **(6 marks)**

(b)   Peer-to-peer file sharing websites which allow users to distribute commercial audio, images and video to other users across networks, including the internet.

.......................................................................................................................................

.......................................................................................................................................

.......................................................................................................................................

.......................................................................................................................................

.......................................................................................................................................

.......................................................................................................................................

....................................................................................................................... **(6 marks)**

(c)   A student noticed that the teacher kept a copy of the password for past examination papers on a post-it note attached to his computer. The student used it to log in as the teacher to take a look.

.......................................................................................................................................

.......................................................................................................................................

.......................................................................................................................................

.......................................................................................................................................

.......................................................................................................................................

.......................................................................................................................................

.......................................................................................................................................

....................................................................................................................... **(6 marks)**

# Cultural issues 1

On this page, you are asked to 'describe' and 'explain'.

Describe means that you have to give a detailed account of a situation, event, or process.

Explain means that you have to give a detailed account including reasons or causes.

1 A school is introducing an automated school registration system.

(a) Two groups of stakeholders who will be affected by the introduction of the new system are the students and their parents.
Identify **one** other group of stakeholders who will be affected.

..................................................................................................................... **(1 mark)**

(b) Explain how the group you have listed in part (a) will be affected.

.....................................................................................................................

.....................................................................................................................

.....................................................................................................................

..................................................................................................................... **(2 marks)**

(c) Some people have poorer access to computer science technology than others.

Make sure that you list different reasons and do not just make different points about the same one!

(i) Give **two** reasons why this is the case.

1 ...............................................................................................................

..................................................................................................................

2 ...............................................................................................................

.................................................................................................................. **(2 marks)**

(ii) Describe **two** ways in which people are affected if they do not have access to computer science technologies such as the internet and broadband.

You have been asked to 'describe' and there are 2 marks for each answer. Ensure that you give full descriptions about the ways people will be affected.

Think about the opportunities that are available with technology, and then think about what it would mean if you were not able to have access to them.

1 ...............................................................................................................

..................................................................................................................

..................................................................................................................

2 ...............................................................................................................

..................................................................................................................

..................................................................................................................

.................................................................................................................. **(4 marks)**

# Cultural issues 2

**1** Discuss the impact of developments in computer science technology on the ways in which people are able to communicate with each other.

> There are many possible answers to this question as you are being asked to discuss the impact of computer science technology. Remember to give both positive and negative effects.
>
> Introduce your arguments briefly. Give examples to support your arguments and briefly summarise your points and draw a conclusion.
>
> The answer has been started for you.

**Guided**

Computer science technology has had a huge impact on the ways in which people communicate.

In areas of the world without telecommunications infrastructure and where there are no land lines, mobile phones have allowed people to communicate using voice calls for the first time.

..........................................................................................................

..........................................................................................................

..........................................................................................................

..........................................................................................................

..........................................................................................................

..........................................................................................................

..........................................................................................................

..........................................................................................................

..........................................................................................................

..........................................................................................................

..........................................................................................................

..........................................................................................................

..........................................................................................................

..........................................................................................................

..........................................................................................................

.................................................................................... **(8 marks)**

# Environmental issues

1   Discuss the positive and negative effects of computer science technology on the environment.

> Remember that you will need an introduction and a conclusion.
>
> Think about what you want to say and make a plan before you start writing your answer. You might find it useful to use headings to remind you of the different topics you need to write about.
>
> Your arguments should be given in a sensibly ordered sequence rather than being random.

..............................................................................................................

..............................................................................................................

..............................................................................................................

..............................................................................................................

..............................................................................................................

..............................................................................................................

..............................................................................................................

..............................................................................................................

..............................................................................................................

..............................................................................................................

..............................................................................................................

..............................................................................................................

..............................................................................................................

..............................................................................................................

..............................................................................................................

..............................................................................................................

..............................................................................................................

..............................................................................................................

..............................................................................................................

..............................................................................................................

..............................................................................................................

..............................................................................................................

..............................................................................................................   **(8 marks)**

# Privacy issues

1   Many people assert that some uses of computer science technology have infringed their right to privacy but others that they are beneficial for society.

Discuss how some uses of computer science technology have an impact on an individual's privacy and how these could also be beneficial for society.

> You could start by making a list of the uses of some relevant computer science technologies, for example surveillance cameras. You then need to consider the impact these have on a person's privacy as well as their benefits.

.............................................................................................................

.............................................................................................................

.............................................................................................................

.............................................................................................................

.............................................................................................................

.............................................................................................................

.............................................................................................................

.............................................................................................................

.............................................................................................................

.............................................................................................................

.............................................................................................................

.............................................................................................................

.............................................................................................................

.............................................................................................................

.............................................................................................................

.............................................................................................................

.............................................................................................................

.............................................................................................................

.............................................................................................................

.............................................................................................................

.............................................................................................................

.............................................................................................................

.............................................................................................................   **(8 marks)**

# Legislation 1

1   A school uses a computerised management system to store details of the students, parents and staff.

(a)   State the legislation which governs how the school can store and use these details.

.......................................................................................................................................

...................................................................................................................... **(1 mark)**

(b)   List **three** rights that people (data subjects) have regarding the data that is stored about them.

1 ...................................................................................................................................

.......................................................................................................................................

2 ...................................................................................................................................

.......................................................................................................................................

3 ...................................................................................................................................

...................................................................................................................... **(3 marks)**

(c)   List **three** responsibilities the school has regarding the collection and storage of the data.

1 ...................................................................................................................................

.......................................................................................................................................

2 ...................................................................................................................................

.......................................................................................................................................

3 ...................................................................................................................................

...................................................................................................................... **(3 marks)**

2   The Computer Misuse Act 1990 identifies three types of offence:
A   Unauthorised access to computer material.
B   Unauthorised modification of computer material.
C   Unauthorised access with intent to commit further offences.

The table below lists some actions that take place in a school.

Complete the table by entering A, B or C in the box beside each action to state the type of offence being committed.

| Action | Type of offence |
|---|---|
| A student accesses another student's email account without permission. | |
| A user accesses parents' stored credit card numbers and security codes in order to buy goods online fraudulently. | |
| A student guesses the login names and passwords of other students and logs into their accounts. | |
| A student gains access to class results and changes their own marks and grades. | |
| As a challenge, a student manages to guess the password of one of the administrative staff to gain entry to the management system. | |

# Legislation 2

1   The Copyright, Designs and Patents Act (1988) is intended to protect the rights of certain individuals.

(a)  What kinds of work are protected under this Act?

........................................................................................................................................

........................................................................................................................ **(1 mark)**

(b)  Who owns the copyright of the work?

........................................................................................................................................

........................................................................................................................ **(1 mark)**

(c)  If internet users illegally download works covered by the Act, legal sanctions can be taken against them.

List **two** of the sanctions.

1 ......................................................................................................................................

2 .............................................................................................................. **(2 marks)**

2   Some copyright holders grant users of their works Creative Commons licences.

(a)  Give **two** reasons why a content creator might consider using a Creative Commons licence to make their work available to others.

1 ......................................................................................................................................

........................................................................................................................................

2 ......................................................................................................................................

........................................................................................................................ **(2 marks)**

(b)  Creative Commons licences that can be given by the copyright holder include public domain, attribution and attribution-non-commercial licences. Describe how a work can be used under each of these licences.

Public domain

........................................................................................................................................

........................................................................................................................................

........................................................................................................................................

Attribution-non-commercial

........................................................................................................................................

........................................................................................................................................

........................................................................................................................ **(4 marks)**

3   State the legislation which governs the rights of access to data held by public authorities.

........................................................................................................................................

........................................................................................................................ **(1 mark)**

**Had a go** ☐    **Nearly there** ☐    **Nailed it!** ☐

# Proprietary and open-source software

**1** TicToc manufactures smart watches. It uses proprietary software to develop apps for the watch.

(a) What is meant by proprietary software?

..................................................................................................................................

.................................................................................................................................. **(1 mark)**

(b) Explain **one** advantage to TicToc of using proprietary software rather than open-source software to develop apps.

..................................................................................................................................

..................................................................................................................................

..................................................................................................................................

.................................................................................................................................. **(2 marks)**

(c) TicToc is considering using open-source software to develop its apps instead of proprietary software.
Describe **one** benefit to users of the smart watch if TicToc decides to use open-source software.

..................................................................................................................................

..................................................................................................................................

..................................................................................................................................

.................................................................................................................................. **(2 marks)**

**2** This table shows some statements about proprietary and open-source software.
Tick the column to show whether the statements apply to proprietary or open-source software.

| Statement | Proprietary | Open-source |
|-----------|-------------|-------------|
| The source code cannot be modified by anyone except the person, team or organisation that created it. | | |
| It is free to use. | | |
| Users can modify the source code to adapt it to their needs and can pass it on to other users free of charge. | | |
| The software must be paid for. | | |
| Users can study the source code to see how the software works. | | |
| It may need specialist knowledge to install the software. | | |
| The support and updates may be expensive. | | |
| The software will be developed carefully and tested thoroughly because people will be paying money to use it and they will be cross if it doesn't work. | | |
| There is a community of dedicated enthusiasts who will provide help and support. | | |

**(4 marks)**

# Computational thinking

1 Danika is creating a computer version of the game 'rock-paper-scissors'. The rules for winning are shown in the figure.

- Rock 'blunts' scissors. Rock wins.
- Scissors 'cut' the paper. Scissors win.
- Paper 'covers' the rock. Paper wins.

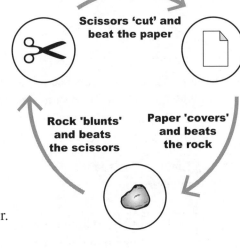

In Danika's game, the computer will take the place of one of the human players and will randomly generate a letter (R, S or P) to represent one of the objects.
She has created a sub-program named 'computerTurn' to generate the computer's letter.

(a) Define what is meant by abstraction.

.................................................................................................................................

................................................................................................................................. **(1 mark)**

(b) Explain why the sub-program 'computerTurn' is an example of abstraction.

.................................................................................................................................

.................................................................................................................................

................................................................................................................................. **(2 marks)**

(c) When both the player and the computer have made a choice, another sub-program decides who has won.
Write an algorithm for this sub-program.

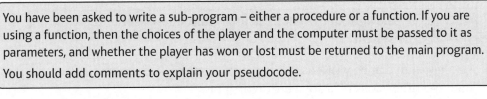

You have been asked to write a sub-program – either a procedure or a function. If you are using a function, then the choices of the player and the computer must be passed to it as parameters, and whether the player has won or lost must be returned to the main program.

You should add comments to explain your pseudocode.

.................................................................................................................................

.................................................................................................................................

.................................................................................................................................

.................................................................................................................................

.................................................................................................................................

.................................................................................................................................

.................................................................................................................................

.................................................................................................................................

.................................................................................................................................

.................................................................................................................................

................................................................................................................................. **(6 marks)**

# Algorithms

**1** (a)  What is an 'algorithm'?

.................................................................................................................................

.................................................................................................................................  **(1 mark)**

(b)  The three constructs used in algorithms are sequence, selection and iteration.
The table below shows an algorithm for authenticating a user's login name and
password, which allows only three attempts.
Enter sequence, selection or iteration in the blank cell.  **(5 marks)**

| Line number | Instruction | Sequence, selection or iteration |
|---|---|---|
| 1 | If username is not recognised, inform the user that the username is not recognised | |
| 2 | Return to step 1 | |
| 3 | If username is recognised, set number of attempts to 1 | |
| 4 | Enter password | |
| 5 | If password does not match the stored password and the number of attempts is less than 3, inform the user that the password is incorrect | |
| 6 | Increase number of attempts by 1 | |
| 7 | Return to step 4 | |
| 8 | If password does not match the stored password and the number of attempts is greater than 3, inform the user they have had three attempts | |
| 9 | Return to step 1 | |
| 10 | If password does match the username, allow user into the system | |

(c)  An algorithm can be written and displayed as plain, written text.
State **two** other ways of displaying algorithms.

1 ...............................................................................................................................

.................................................................................................................................

2 ...............................................................................................................................

.................................................................................................................................  **(2 marks)**

# Algorithms – pseudocode

1  (a)  Define what is meant by the term 'pseudocode'.

........................................................................................................................

........................................................................................................................

........................................................................................................................

........................................................................................................................  **(2 marks)**

(b)  Write an algorithm in pseudocode to convert an 8-bit binary number into a decimal (denary) number. You can assume that the binary number is correctly formatted as 1s and 0s and has the correct number of digits so that validation is not required.

> The algorithm should examine each of the 8 binary digits and multiply them by their place values. It should then find the total of these multiplications. See page 74 of the Revision Guide for a reminder on converting binary to denary.
>
> You will not have access to the pseudocode guide in the exam, but you are not expected to memorise it. Make sure your pseudocode is clear, concise and accurate, and answers the question.

........................................................................................................................

........................................................................................................................

........................................................................................................................

........................................................................................................................

........................................................................................................................

........................................................................................................................

........................................................................................................................

........................................................................................................................

........................................................................................................................

........................................................................................................................

........................................................................................................................

........................................................................................................................

........................................................................................................................

........................................................................................................................

........................................................................................................................

........................................................................................................................  **(6 marks)**

# Algorithms – flow diagrams

1   The algorithm for a game simulates the throwing of three dice to find the player's score.

   • If all three are equal, then the score is the total of the dice.

   • If two are equal, the score is equal to the sum of the two equal dice minus the third.

   • If none are equal, then the score is zero.

   Here is part of a flow diagram for the algorithm.

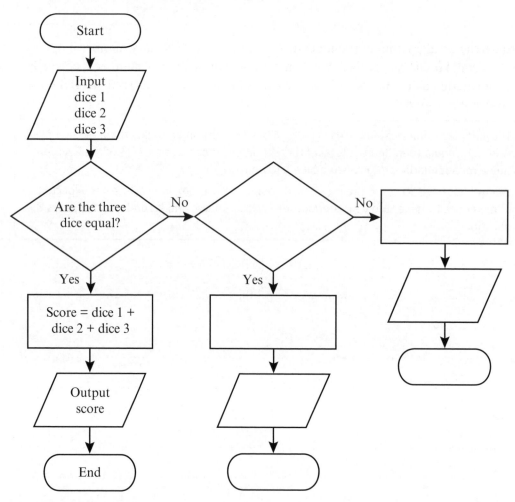

   (a)  Complete the flow diagram for the algorithm.   **(6 marks)**

   (b)  Use the algorithm to calculate the score from the following dice throws.

   3 6 3

   .................................................................................................................

   5 4 5

   .................................................................................................................   **(2 marks)**

   (c)  It is possible to obtain a negative score using the algorithm.
        State **three** dice numbers which would result in a negative score.

   .................................................................................................................   **(1 mark)**

# Standard searching algorithms – linear search

1 (a) Describe how a linear search algorithm works.

.................................................................................................................

.................................................................................................................

.................................................................................................................

................................................................................................................. **(2 marks)**

(b) David has compiled a list of all the people invited to his party and has stored the names in an array called partyList.
Write an algorithm in pseudocode to check whether Elaine's name is on the list.

> The answer should, if possible, be written in the OCR pseudocode, but you may use any style of pseudocode providing its meaning can be understood by a competent programmer.
>
> Remember to use comments to explain your pseudocode.

.................................................................................................................

.................................................................................................................

.................................................................................................................

.................................................................................................................

.................................................................................................................

.................................................................................................................

.................................................................................................................

.................................................................................................................

.................................................................................................................

.................................................................................................................

.................................................................................................................

.................................................................................................................

.................................................................................................................

.................................................................................................................

.................................................................................................................

.................................................................................................................

................................................................................................................. **(6 marks)**

# Standard searching algorithms – binary search

1   Describe the stages of a binary search on a list of items sorted in ascending order.

..................................................................................................................................

..................................................................................................................................

..................................................................................................................................

..................................................................................................................................

..................................................................................................................................

..................................................................................................................................

..................................................................................................................................

..................................................................................................  **(2 marks)**

2   A student has the following list of friends.

| Ahmed | Ann | Claire | David | Mary | Matt | Peter | Stephen | Zoe |
|-------|-----|--------|-------|------|------|-------|---------|-----|

Show the stages of a binary search to find the name 'Stephen' from the data shown in the list.

> You should indicate which item will be selected each time and then show the new sub-list.

..................................................................................................................................

..................................................................................................................................

..................................................................................................................................

..................................................................................................................................

..................................................................................................................................

..................................................................................................  **(4 marks)**

3   Show the stages of a binary search to find the number '9' from the data shown in this table.

| 1 | 6 | 9 | 13 | 15 | 21 | 28 | 36 | 42 | 69 | 76 | 85 | 94 |
|---|---|---|----|----|----|----|----|----|----|----|----|----|

..................................................................................................................................

..................................................................................................................................

..................................................................................................................................

..................................................................................................................................

..................................................................................................................................

..................................................................................................  **(4 marks)**

# Comparing linear and binary searches

 1   Complete the flow diagram of a binary search by labelling the empty symbols.        **(5 marks)**

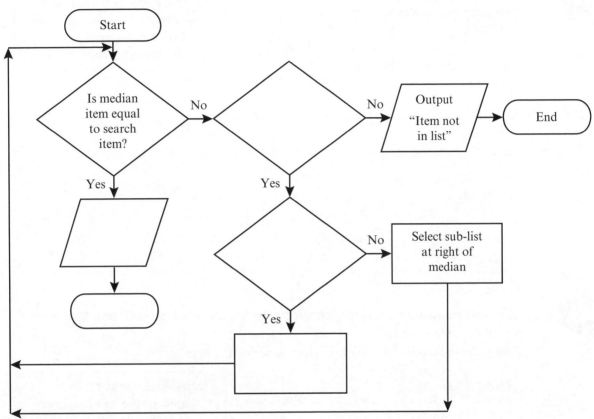

 2   (a)   When searching a list of 100 items, the largest number of comparisons a linear
          search would have to make would be 100.
          Show that the maximum possible number of comparisons made using a binary
          search of the same list would be 7. Show your working.

          .................................................................................................................................

          .................................................................................................................................

          .................................................................................................................................

          .................................................................................................................................

          .................................................................................................................................

          .................................................................................................................................        **(4 marks)**

       (b)   A binary search is generally more efficient than a linear search. However, this is
          not always the case.
          Explain why using a linear search may be quicker than using a binary search in
          some circumstances.

          .................................................................................................................................

          .................................................................................................................................

          .................................................................................................................................

          .................................................................................................................................        **(2 marks)**

# Standard sorting algorithms – bubble sort

**1** This list of numbers must be sorted into ascending order.

| 20 | 15 | 3 | 13 | 9 | 2 | 6 |
|----|----|---|----|---|---|---|

Show the stages of a bubble sort when applied to the data shown in the list.

> You should label each pass and remember to compare each pair of numbers and switch them round if they are not in the correct order.

...................................................................................................................

...................................................................................................................

...................................................................................................................

...................................................................................................................

...................................................................................................................

................................................................................................................... **(4 marks)**

**2** The table below shows an algorithm for carrying out a bubble sort, but the lines are not in the correct order.
Complete the table to show the correct order of the lines.

| Order | Line |
|-------|------|
| 1 | swapped = True |
|   | next index |
|   | for index = 1 to list.length – 1 |
| 3 | swapped = False |
|   | if list[index – 1] > list[index] then |
|   | swapped = True |
| 10 | endif |
| 6 | temp = list[index – 1] |
|   | while swapped = True |
|   | list[index – 1] = list[index] |
|   | endwhile |
|   | list[index] = temp |

> A loop will need to be set up to move through the list to compare the adjacent values and swap them if they are in the wrong order. It will have to run until there are no swaps.
>
> The best responses should:
> - place the start and end of the while loop in the correct positions
> - order the lines of the swap correctly
> - put the start and end of the if statements in the correct positions
> - set the value of the swapped variable correctly.

**(5 marks)**

# Standard sorting algorithms – insertion sort

**1** Describe the stages of the insertion sort algorithm as it sorts data into ascending order.

..................................................................................................................................

..................................................................................................................................

..................................................................................................................................

..................................................................................................................................

..................................................................................................................................

..................................................................................................................................

..................................................................................................................................

.................................................................................................................... **(4 marks)**

**2** Use an insertion sort to put the data shown in the table into ascending order.
Write down all the stages of the process.

| 6 | 3 | 12 | 9 | 7 | 11 | 1 |
|---|---|----|---|---|----|---|
|   |   |    |   |   |    |   |
|   |   |    |   |   |    |   |
|   |   |    |   |   |    |   |
|   |   |    |   |   |    |   |
|   |   |    |   |   |    |   |
|   |   |    |   |   |    |   |

**(6 marks)**

**3** Use an insertion sort to put the data shown in the table into ascending order.
Write down all the stages of the process.

| Ravish | Sean | Elsie | Alice | Rosie | Jack | Ollie |
|--------|------|-------|-------|-------|------|-------|
|        |      |       |       |       |      |       |
|        |      |       |       |       |      |       |
|        |      |       |       |       |      |       |
|        |      |       |       |       |      |       |
|        |      |       |       |       |      |       |
|        |      |       |       |       |      |       |

**(5 marks)**

# Standard searching algorithms – merge sort

1  (a)  The merge sort algorithm divides up a list into smaller and smaller sections and then sorts them into order before putting them back together again.
Explain the advantage of using this technique.

.......................................................................................................................................

.......................................................................................................................................

.......................................................................................................................................

.......................................................................................................................  **(2 marks)**

(b)  The merge sort algorithm makes use of recursion.
Define what is meant by recursion.

.......................................................................................................................................

.......................................................................................................................  **(1 mark)**

2  Use a merge sort to put the data shown below into ascending order.
Show all the stages of the process.

| 33 | 25 | 46 | 2 | 8 | 69 | 9 |
|----|----|----|---|---|----|---|

.......................................................................................................................................

.......................................................................................................................................

.......................................................................................................................................

.......................................................................................................................................

.......................................................................................................................................

.......................................................................................................................................

.......................................................................................................................................

.......................................................................................................................................

.......................................................................................................................................

.......................................................................................................................................

.......................................................................................................................................

.......................................................................................................................................

.......................................................................................................................................

.......................................................................................................................................

.......................................................................................................................  **(6 marks)**

# Interpreting, correcting and completing algorithms

1   Rosie is writing an algorithm to work out the change to be given to a customer in a car park payment system.
This flow diagram is incomplete and does not show all the possible combinations of notes and coins.

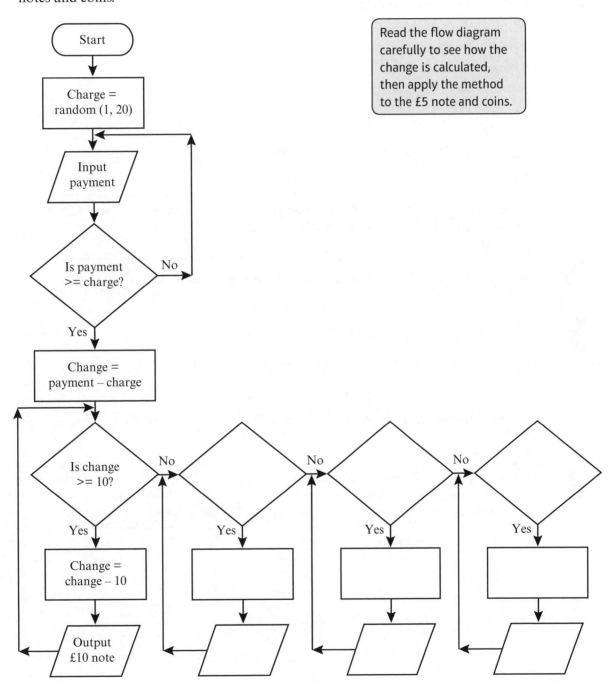

> Read the flow diagram carefully to see how the change is calculated, then apply the method to the £5 note and coins.

Complete the flow diagram to show how the numbers of £5 notes and £2 and £1 coins in the change will be calculated. Write your answer in the empty symbols.   **(6 marks)**

# Using trace tables

1   This algorithm is designed to search for a value in a list.

```
1    list = [5, 9, 2, 5, 13]
2    item = input("Please enter the search item.")
3    found = False
4    for search = 0 to list.length
5        if item == list[search] then
6            found = True
7        endif
8    next search
9    if found == True then
10       print("The item is in the list.")
11   else
12       print("The item is not in the list.")
13   endif
```

> Before you start, read through the algorithm very carefully. Make sure that you understand what the algorithm is intended to do. That will help you to find the error in the code in part (b).

(a)   Identify the data structure used to store the numbers in the list.

.............................................................................................................................. **(1 mark)**

(b)   There is an error in the code.

    (i)   State the number of the line in which there is an error.

.............................................................................................................................. **(1 mark)**

    (ii) Give the correct version of this code.

.............................................................................................................................. **(1 mark)**

(c)   Complete the following trace table for the corrected version of the algorithm.

| item | found | search | list[search] | output |
|------|-------|--------|--------------|--------|
| 13 | False | 0 | 5 | |
| | | | | |
| | | | | |
| | | | | |
| | | | | |
| | | | | |

**(5 marks)**

# Variables and constants

1   Computer code makes use of variables and constants.

(a)   Explain what is meant by a variable.

..................................................................................................................................

.................................................................................................................................. **(2 marks)**

(b)   State how a constant differs from a variable.

..................................................................................................................................

.................................................................................................................................. **(1 mark)**

(c)   Variables and constants must be given identifiers which should be consistent throughout the program.
State why variables and constants should be given meaningful names.

..................................................................................................................................

.................................................................................................................................. **(1 mark)**

(d)   The algorithm shown below searches for a value in a list.

```
1    mysteryNumber = 6
2    correct = False
3    while correct == False
4        guess = input("Please enter a number between 1 and 10")
5        if guess == mysteryNumber then
6            correct = True
7        endif
8    endwhile
```

Complete the table to show the variables used and why they are used in the program.

> Read the algorithm carefully to identify the variables and to understand why they have been used. The first one has been done for you.

**Guided**

| Variable | Use within the program |
|----------|------------------------|
| mysteryNumber | This is used to hold the number which must be guessed. |
| | |
| | |
| | |

**(6 marks)**

# Arithmetic operators

**1** Evaluate the following equation using the correct order of operations. Show the result of each stage.
The first one has been done for you.

result = 6 * 8 / 2 + (15 – 6) + 3^3

> **Guided**

result = 6 * 8 / 2 + 9 + 3^3

.............................................................................................................

.............................................................................................................

.............................................................................................................

.............................................................................................................    **(3 marks)**

**2** Complete the table below by filling in the value of number after each line of code is executed. The first one has been done for you.

> **Guided**

| Code | Resultnumber |
|------|--------------|
| number = 12 + 6 / 2 | number = 15 |
| number = 6 * 3 / 2 | |
| number = 23 MOD 6 | |
| number = 23 DIV 6 | |
| number = 6 ^ 2 | |

**(4 marks)**

**3** A number trick asks you to think of a number, double it, add six, divide it in half and then subtract the number you started with. The result should always be 3.
Write an algorithm using pseudocode that asks a user to input a number, then carries out each of the operations and outputs the result.

> Read the question very carefully to identify all the arithmetic operations needed. You should see that you will need two variables to store the numbers!
>
> Do a dry run of your algorithm to check that the result is correct.

.............................................................................................................

.............................................................................................................

.............................................................................................................

.............................................................................................................

.............................................................................................................

.............................................................................................................

.............................................................................................................

.............................................................................................................

.............................................................................................................

.............................................................................................................

.............................................................................................................    **(3 marks)**

# Comparison operators

1  Complete the table below by evaluating each of the statements listed and stating whether it is True or False.
The first one has been done for you.

> You first need to work out the results of the calculations and then compare them using the operators.

| Statement | True/False |
|---|---|
| 7 * 3 != 10 + 11 | False |
| 8 + 10 > 8 * 2 | |
| 9 * 3 <= 10 + 17 | |
| 10 + 15 >= 6 * 5 | |
| 9 * 2 == 6 * 3 | |

**(5 marks)**

2  Alina has stored her computer science marks in an array named 'marks'.
Write an algorithm using pseudocode that prompts Alina to enter a new mark and then outputs the number of marks in the array that are:

equal to it
less than it
greater than it.

.......................................................................................................

.......................................................................................................

.......................................................................................................

.......................................................................................................

.......................................................................................................

.......................................................................................................

.......................................................................................................

.......................................................................................................

.......................................................................................................

.......................................................................................................

.......................................................................................................

.......................................................................................................

.......................................................................................................

.......................................................................................................

.......................................................................................................

.......................................................................................................

.......................................................................................................

....................................................................................................... **(6 marks)**

# Boolean operators

**1** Complete the table below to show the output of each algorithm.
The first solution has been completed for you.

> Read and work through the algorithms carefully and write the expected outcome in the second column.

**Guided**

| Algorithm | Output |
|---|---|
| ```
number = 3
if number > 0 AND number < 2 then
    print("Within range.")
else
    print("Out of range.")
endif
``` | Out of range. |
| ```
number = 6
if NOT(number = 3) OR number != 5 then
    print("Number is acceptable.")
else
    print("Number is not acceptable.")
endif
``` | |
| ```
colour = "red"
size = "m"
price = 25
if colour = "blue" OR colour = "red" AND size == "m"
AND price <= 30 then
    print("This would be OK.")
else
    print("Not OK.")
endif
``` | |
| ```
number1 = 6
number2 = 9
if (number1 <= 9 OR number2 >=10) AND NOT(number1 *
number2 <50) AND (number2 - number1 == 3) then
    print("These numbers are OK.")
else
    print("Not OK.")
endif
``` | |

**(3 marks)**

# Selection

1   A teacher wants a program that will output a comment when a mark is input, according to the following rules.

| Mark | Comment |
|------|---------|
| 90 and above | Excellent |
| 70 to 89 | Very good |
| 60 to 69 | Good |
| 50 to 59 | Satisfactory |
| Below 50 | Unsatisfactory |

The algorithm should allow the teacher to enter a mark and then use comparison operators to decide the range the mark is in and display the appropriate comment.

Be careful when you are selecting the ranges. A mark can only be put in one range.

Write an algorithm using pseudocode that prompts the teacher to enter a mark and then displays the appropriate comment.

..........................................................................................................................

..........................................................................................................................

..........................................................................................................................

..........................................................................................................................

..........................................................................................................................

..........................................................................................................................

..........................................................................................................................

..........................................................................................................................

..........................................................................................................................

..........................................................................................................................

..........................................................................................................................

..........................................................................................................................

..........................................................................................................................

..........................................................................................................................

..........................................................................................................................

..........................................................................................................................

..........................................................................................................................

..........................................................................................................................

..........................................................................................................................

..........................................................................................................................   **(5 marks)**

# Iteration

**1** The algorithm shown below searches for a value in a list.

```
list = [5, 9, 2, 5, 13]
item = input("Please enter the search item.")
found = False
for search = 0 to list.length -1
    if item == list[search] then
        found = True
    endif
next search
if found == True then
    print("The item is in the list")
else
    print("The item is not in the list.")
endif
```

The algorithm is not very efficient because it continues iterating through the list even if the search item has been found.
Rewrite the algorithm to improve the efficiency by stopping the search when the item has been found.

> You need to change the algorithm so that it breaks out of the loop if the item is found.
>
> Remember – there is another type of loop!

..................................................................................................................

..................................................................................................................

..................................................................................................................

..................................................................................................................

..................................................................................................................

..................................................................................................................

..................................................................................................................

..................................................................................................................

..................................................................................................................

..................................................................................................................

..................................................................................................................

..................................................................................................................

..................................................................................................................

..................................................................................................................

.......................................................................................................... **(4 marks)**

# Data types

1   The following algorithm allows a user to enter data about themselves and the number of whole hours they worked each day for a week.

```
name = input("Please enter your name")
gender = input("Please enter your gender as 'F' or 'M'")
daysWorked = input("Enter the number of days you worked this week.")
if daysWorked = 5 then
    fullWeek = True
endif
if fullWeek = True then
    hoursWorked = 0
    for day = 1 to 5
        oneDay = input("Please enter complete hours worked for day " + day + ".")
        hoursWorked = hoursWorked + oneDay
    next day
    meanHoursWorked = hoursWorked / 5
    print("Mean hours worked per day this week = " + meanHoursWorked)
else
    print("Five day week not worked.")
endif
```

(a)   Complete the table below by giving an example of a variable used in the algorithm above for each of the data types listed.
The first one has been done for you.

> Guided

| Data type | Variable |
|-----------|----------|
| String | name |
| Real | |
| Boolean | |
| Integer | |
| Character | |

**(5 marks)**

(b)   The algorithm is to be extended to calculate the user's weekly pay.
State **two** additional variables that will be needed and identify the data type of each.

Variable 1

......................................................................................................................................

Data type

......................................................................................................................................

Variable 2

......................................................................................................................................

Data type

...................................................................................................................................... **(4 marks)**

# String manipulation

1   The following algorithm is designed to manipulate a string.

```
subject = "Computer Science"
for index = 0 to subject.length - 1
    if subject(index) == " " then
        position = index
    endif
next index
print(position)
partSubject = subject(3, 3)
```

Complete the table below by stating the values of the variables listed.

| Variable | Value |
|----------|-------|
| subject.length | |
| position | |
| partSubject | |

**(3 marks)**

2   Write an algorithm using pseudocode that will analyse a sentence entered by a user and output the number of times each vowel occurs in the sentence.

> You need to find the length of the string so that the algorithm can traverse it to find the vowels.
>
> Remember that vowels are the letters a, e, i, o and u. The algorithm must be able to count upper and lower case letters as the same vowel.

.......................................................................................................

.......................................................................................................

.......................................................................................................

.......................................................................................................

.......................................................................................................

.......................................................................................................

.......................................................................................................

.......................................................................................................

.......................................................................................................

.......................................................................................................

.......................................................................................................

.......................................................................................................

.......................................................................................................   **(5 marks)**

# Arrays

1 (a) Describe what is meant by an array.

...................................................................................................................

...................................................................................................................

...................................................................................................................

................................................................................................................... **(2 marks)**

Jack is going to take his temperature every day for a week and would like to store the readings in an array.

(b) (i) Write the pseudocode to declare an array named 'temp' to store the temperature data.

.................................................................................................................... **(1 mark)**

(ii) Jack is going to take his temperature every day for a week (°C) and would like to store the readings in an array.

...................................................................................................................

...................................................................................................................

...................................................................................................................

...................................................................................................................

...................................................................................................................

...................................................................................................................

...................................................................................................................

...................................................................................................................

...................................................................................................................

...................................................................................................................

...................................................................................................................

................................................................................................................... **(4 marks)**

2 The figure shows a black and white bitmap image.
The image can be encoded using 1 to represent black pixels and 0 to represent white pixels.

**Guided**

Complete the matrix below to show how the pixel data could be stored in a two-dimensional array.
The first row has been done for you.

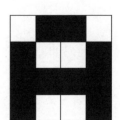

|   | 0 | 1 | 2 | 3 |
|---|---|---|---|---|
| 0 | O | 1 | 1 | O |
| 1 |   |   |   |   |
| 2 |   |   |   |   |
| 3 |   |   |   |   |

**(3 marks)**

59

# File handling operations

1   The figure shows a black and white bitmap image.
    This image can be encoded into a string named 'pixels' using
    1 to represent black and 0 to represent white pixels.

(a)  Write an algorithm using pseudocode to store the pixel
     data in a text file named 'shape.txt'.

...................................................................................................

...................................................................................................

...................................................................................................

...................................................................................................

...................................................................................................

...................................................................................................

...................................................................................................   **(4 marks)**

(b)  Write an algorithm using pseudocode that would read the data from the file
     'shape.txt' into a two-dimensional array named 'matrix'.

> Even if you aren't sure if you can answer the whole question, there may be parts you do
> know. For example, if you can't write the whole algorithm, you may pick up marks for
> opening and closing files correctly.

...................................................................................................

...................................................................................................

...................................................................................................

...................................................................................................

...................................................................................................

...................................................................................................

...................................................................................................

...................................................................................................

...................................................................................................

...................................................................................................

...................................................................................................

...................................................................................................   **(6 marks)**

# Records

1  Mrs Jackson is opening a cattery to look after animals when their owners go on holiday.
   She has created a database table to store the details of the cats. Some of the data is shown in the table below.

> Records allow users to store items of data about particular entities, in this case cats.
> Unlike arrays, records can store items of different data types.

| Name | Gender | Weight(Kg) | Number of days | Special diet? |
|------|--------|------------|----------------|---------------|
| Dottie | F | 3.2 | 6 | N |
| Jack | M | 4.2 | 7 | Y |
| ................... | ................... | ................... | ................... | ................... |

(a) The table stores several items of information about each cat.
     Annotate the table to show:

     (i)  a field                                                              **(1 mark)**

     (ii) a record.                                                            **(1 mark)**

(b) State a suitable data type for each item of information in the empty row in the table.                                                                    **(5 marks)**

(c) State a validation check that could be carried out on the 'gender' data.

    ...................................................................................................

    ...................................................................................................

    ...................................................................................................

    ...................................................................................................  **(2 marks)**

(d) (i)  Explain why none of the fields in the table would be suitable as the key field.

    ...................................................................................................

    ...................................................................................................

    ...................................................................................................

    ...................................................................................................  **(2 marks)**

    (ii) Outline how Mrs Jackson could add a suitable key field to her table.

    ...................................................................................................

    ...................................................................................................  **(1 mark)**

# Structured query language

1   Sam has created a database of his music collection. The details of each track are stored in a table called Collection. A sample of the data is shown in the table below.

| ItemNumber | Title | Artist | Length | TimesPlayed | Medium |
|---|---|---|---|---|---|
| 001 | When you go | Charlie Charles | 3.5 | 10 | CD |
| 002 | Down in the groove | Sue Strange | 2.5 | 6 | CD |
| 003 | Where have you gone? | The Strangers | 1.6 | 12 | Vinyl |
| 004 | One day | The Strangers | 2.5 | 15 | Vinyl |
| 005 | Sunshine and rain | Sue Strange | 4.3 | 0 | Vinyl |
| 006 | It blew in the wind | Bob Guthrie | 6.5 | 21 | CD |
| 007 | One more time | Charlie Charles | 2.6 | 8 | Vinyl |

Here is a query that is run against this database table.

```
SELECT * FROM COLLECTION
WHERE Length > 2.5;
```

(a)   How many records are returned from running this query?

..................................................................................................................... **(1 mark)**

(b)   Complete the WHERE clause in this query to find records for all the songs that Sam has played at least 15 times.

> Make sure that you use the correct comparison operator.
>
> SQL commands are given in the pseudocode guide. You are not expected to memorise them, but you should try to use them here.

```
SELECT *
FROM COLLECTION
WHERE ...........................................................................
```
**(2 marks)**

(c)   (i)   Write down the SQL command that Sam used to return these records from the table Collection.

| When you go | 3.5 | CD |
|---|---|---|
| One more time | 2.6 | Vinyl |

..................................................................................................................

..................................................................................................................

.................................................................................................................. **(3 marks)**

(ii)   Write down the SQL command that Sam used to return these records from the table Collection.

| When you go | 10 | CD |
|---|---|---|
| It blew in the wind | 21 | CD |
| One more time | 8 | Vinyl |

..................................................................................................................

..................................................................................................................

.................................................................................................................. **(4 marks)**

# Sub-programs 1

**1** When writing programs, computer scientists make use of sub-programs.

(a) Explain what is meant by a sub-program.

.......................................................................................................................

.......................................................................................................................

.......................................................................................................................

....................................................................................................................... **(2 marks)**

(b) Describe **two** advantages to a programmer of using sub-programs.

1 ....................................................................................................................

.......................................................................................................................

.......................................................................................................................

2 ....................................................................................................................

.......................................................................................................................

.......................................................................................................................

....................................................................................................................... **(4 marks)**

(c) Two types of sub-program are functions and procedures.
State **one** difference between these types of sub-program.

.......................................................................................................................

.......................................................................................................................

.......................................................................................................................

....................................................................................................................... **(1 mark)**

**2** This is a function to convert centimetres to inches.

```
1   function centimetresToInches(measurement)
2       newMeasurement = measurement/2.54
3
4   endfunction
```

(a) State the name of one parameter used in the function.

....................................................................................................................... **(1 mark)**

(b) State **one** local variable used in the function.

....................................................................................................................... **(1 mark)**

(c) Line 3 is missing. Complete line 3.

.......................................................................................................................

....................................................................................................................... **(2 marks)**

# Sub-programs 2

1  The algorithm below uses a sub-program to find the area and circumference of rectangles.

```
1   function calculate(length, width)
2       area = length * width
3       circumference = 2*length + 2*width
4       return area, circumference
5   endfunction
6   //This is the main program
7   recLength = input("Please enter the length.")
8   recWidth = input("Please enter the width.")
9
10  print(recArea + recCircumference)
```

(a)  Identify **two** global variables used in the algorithm.

1 ....................................................................................................................................

2 ....................................................................................................................................  **(2 marks)**

(b)  Identify **two** parameters used in the algorithm.

1 ....................................................................................................................................

2 ....................................................................................................................................  **(2 marks)**

(c)  Identify **two** local variables used in the algorithm.

1 ....................................................................................................................................

2 ....................................................................................................................................  **(2 marks)**

(d)  Line 9 is missing.
Complete line 9 to call the function.

....................................................................................................................................  **(2 marks)**

2  Write an algorithm using pseudocode that uses a function to find the larger of any two different numbers entered by a user.

....................................................................................................................................

....................................................................................................................................

....................................................................................................................................

....................................................................................................................................

....................................................................................................................................

....................................................................................................................................

....................................................................................................................................

....................................................................................................................................

....................................................................................................................................  **(6 marks)**

# Defensive design

1 Advika has decided to incorporate user authentication into her program. Users must register a username and password. A password must have at least eight characters, at least one of which must be an upper case letter.

Use pseudocode to write a suitable password creation algorithm for Advika's program. The algorithm should include a check that a password has been entered and a check on the password requirements.

> Your algorithm should check that the user has actually made an entry and that the correct number of characters has been used. You also have to check that an upper case letter has been used.
>
> Remember: you can check for upper case letters using their ASCII code values.

..........................................................................................................................

..........................................................................................................................

..........................................................................................................................

..........................................................................................................................

..........................................................................................................................

..........................................................................................................................

..........................................................................................................................

..........................................................................................................................

..........................................................................................................................

..........................................................................................................................

..........................................................................................................................

..........................................................................................................................

..........................................................................................................................

..........................................................................................................................

..........................................................................................................................

..........................................................................................................................

..........................................................................................................................

..........................................................................................................................

..........................................................................................................................

..........................................................................................................................

..........................................................................................................................

.......................................................................................................................... **(8 marks)**

# Testing and maintainability

1  Mr Smart has written a program so that he can input the students' exam percentages into an array named 'marks' in the same order as the students' names stored in an array named 'students' that already contains their surnames. The program should also output the name of the student with the highest percentage.

```
1   maximum = 0
2   for index = 0 to students.length
3   percentage = input("Please enter the percentage mark for " + students[index])
4   while percentage > 100 OR percentage < 0
5       percentage = input("Percentage must be 100 or less. Please enter
        the percentage mark for " + students[index])
6   endwhile
7   marks[0] = percentage
8   if percentage < maximum then
9           maximum = index
10  endif
11  next index
12  print("The student with the maximum mark is" + students[maximum])
```

Mr Smart has selected some data to test the program.

(a) Complete the table below to show the type of test and the expected result, based on the given test data.

> Look at page 66 of the Revision Guide to identify the type of test carried out in each case and then state the expected results. Will the data be accepted or not?

| Test number | Type of test | Test data | Expected result |
|:-----------:|:------------:|:---------:|:---------------:|
| 1 | | 69 | |
| 2 | | 99 | |
| 3 | | 120 | |

**(6 marks)**

(b) There are **three** errors in Mr Smart's code.
Write down the line numbers and the correct versions of the code in the table below.

| Line number | Correct version |
|:-----------:|:---------------:|
| | |
| | |
| | |

**(6 marks)**

# Computational logic 1

1   Identify the following logic gates.

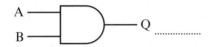

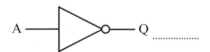

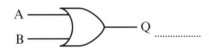

**(3 marks)**

2   Complete the truth table below for this logic diagram.

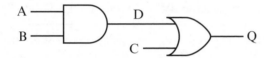

The first one has been done for you.

| A | B | C | D | Q |
|---|---|---|---|---|
| 0 | 0 | 0 | O | O |
| 0 | 0 | 1 | | |
| 0 | 1 | 0 | | |
| 0 | 1 | 1 | | |
| 1 | 0 | 0 | | |
| 1 | 0 | 1 | | |
| 1 | 1 | 0 | | |
| 1 | 1 | 1 | | |

**(6 marks)**

3   An alarm system uses three switches – A, B and C. Switch C is the master switch and the alarm will not sound unless it is on. The alarm will then sound when either switches A or B are on.
Draw a logic diagram for this system.

> Be careful when drawing your logic diagram – make sure that each gate is clearly identifiable.

**(3 marks)**

# Computational logic 2

1  The following logic diagram shows the expression P = NOT(A) AND B

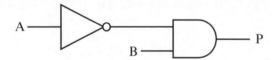

Complete the truth table for this logic diagram.

| A | B | P |
|---|---|---|
| 0 | 0 | |
| 0 | 1 | |
| 1 | 0 | |
| 1 | 1 | |

**(2 marks)**

2  (a)  Draw a logic diagram for the Boolean statement P = (A OR B) AND NOT(C).

> Read the statement very carefully and note the position of the brackets. Make sure they are represented correctly in the diagram.

Logic diagram

**(3 marks)**

(b)  Complete the truth table below to show the value of P = (A OR B) AND NOT (C) for each possible set of values of A, B and C.

| A | B | C | P |
|---|---|---|---|
| 0 | 0 | 0 | |
| 0 | 0 | 1 | |
| 0 | 1 | 0 | |
| 0 | 1 | 1 | |
| 1 | 0 | 0 | |
| 1 | 0 | 1 | |
| 1 | 1 | 0 | |
| 1 | 1 | 1 | |

**(4 marks)**

# Programming languages

1   The same program has been written in three different languages, as shown below.

> You need to be able to recognise low- and high-level languages and the form in which they are written.

| Language 1 | Language 2 | Language 3 |
|---|---|---|
| firstNumber = 1<br>secondNumber = 2<br>total = a + b | LD 1<br>ADD 2<br>STORE 3 | 00111110<br>00000001<br>00000110<br>00000010<br>10000000 |

(a)  State the name of language 2. ................................................................... **(1 mark)**

(b)  State the name of language 3. ................................................................... **(1 mark)**

(c)  Explain why language 1 is a high-level language, while languages 2 and 3 are low-level languages.

...................................................................................................................

...................................................................................................................

...................................................................................................................

................................................................................................................... **(2 marks)**

(d)  (i)  Describe **two** advantages for a programmer of writing programs in a high-level language.

1 ...............................................................................................................

...................................................................................................................

...................................................................................................................

2 ...............................................................................................................

...................................................................................................................

................................................................................................................... **(4 marks)**

(ii)  Describe **two** advantages for a programmer of writing programs in a low-level language.

1 ...............................................................................................................

...................................................................................................................

...................................................................................................................

2 ...............................................................................................................

...................................................................................................................

................................................................................................................... **(4 marks)**

# Translators

1   Computers can only execute instructions written in machine code.

(a)   State the name of the software used to translate a program written in assembly language into machine code.

....................................................................................................................................

....................................................................................................................................   **(1 mark)**

(b)   Both compilers and interpreters translate high-level program code into machine code.
Compare the method of translation used by each.

....................................................................................................................................

....................................................................................................................................

....................................................................................................................................   **(2 marks)**

(c)   Outline **one** advantage and **one** disadvantage of each method for programmers and users.

Compiler

....................................................................................................................................

....................................................................................................................................

....................................................................................................................................

....................................................................................................................................

Interpreter

....................................................................................................................................

....................................................................................................................................

....................................................................................................................................   **(4 marks)**

2   A programmer is writing software for a new set-top receiver for satellite TV. Explain why the programmer should use a compiler instead of an interpreter to translate the code.

....................................................................................................................................

....................................................................................................................................   **(2 marks)**

# Integrated development environment

**1** Ahmed's code has some syntax errors.

(a) What is meant by a syntax error? Give an example.

.............................................................................................................

.............................................................................................................

.............................................................................................................

.............................................................................................................  **(2 marks)**

(b) Ahmed's friends advised him to use an IDE (integrated development environment). Describe **two** tools and facilities available in an IDE which can help the programmer to avoid syntax errors.

> Do not just write about any available tools. They must be ones that will prevent or identify syntax errors, and you must explain how the features help to reduce syntax errors.

1 ............................................................................................................

.............................................................................................................

.............................................................................................................

.............................................................................................................

2 ............................................................................................................

.............................................................................................................

.............................................................................................................

.............................................................................................................  **(4 marks)**

(c) An IDE also provides other facilities for programmers.
State the purpose of the functions of the following facilities.

Variable tracing

.............................................................................................................

.............................................................................................................

.............................................................................................................

.............................................................................................................

.............................................................................................................

Breakpoints

.............................................................................................................

.............................................................................................................

.............................................................................................................

.............................................................................................................

.............................................................................................................  **(2 marks)**

# Data representation

1 (a) State the format required for data to be processed by a computer.

.................................................................................................................................... **(1 mark)**

(b) Explain why instructions and data must be in this format.

....................................................................................................................................

....................................................................................................................................

.................................................................................................................................... **(2 marks)**

2 The following table shows the units of data storage capacity.
Complete the table to show the order of magnitude of the units, from smallest to largest. Two have been filled in for you.

**Guided**

| byte | megabyte | terabyte | bit | petabyte | kilobyte | gigabyte | nibble |
|------|----------|----------|-----|----------|----------|----------|--------|
|      | 5        |          | 1   |          |          |          |        |

**(3 marks)**

3 A file has a size of 72 000 000 000 bits.
Calculate the file size in megabytes and gigabytes using the decimal prefix, i.e. use 1000 instead of 1024. Show your working.

megabytes

gigabytes.

**(2 marks)**

4 Calculate how many bits there are in a file with a size of 20 megabytes.
Show your working.

**(1 mark)**

# Converting from denary to binary

1  Convert the decimal (denary) number 199 into an 8-bit binary number.
   You must show your working.

> Remember to compare the decimal number with the binary place value and calculate the remainder.
>
> You should always show your working in questions involving calculations. You may get some credit for showing that you understand the method even if the answer you come up with is wrong.

**(2 marks)**

2  Write an algorithm in pseudocode to convert a whole decimal number between 0 and 255 into an 8-bit binary number.

> You might want to use a data structure to store the place values that you are going to use and another one to store the digits of the binary number.

..................................................................................................................................

..................................................................................................................................

..................................................................................................................................

..................................................................................................................................

..................................................................................................................................

..................................................................................................................................

..................................................................................................................................

..................................................................................................................................

..................................................................................................................................

..................................................................................................................................

..................................................................................................................................

..................................................................................................................................

..................................................................................................................................

..................................................................................................................................

..................................................................................................................................  **(8 marks)**

Had a go ☐    Nearly there ☐    Nailed it! ☐

# Converting from binary to denary and binary addition

**1** Convert the 8-bit binary number 10010111 into a decimal (denary) number.
You must show your working.

> Remember to multiply the binary digits by their place values. You could use a table to help you to do this.

**(2 marks)**

**2** Add the following 8-bit binary numbers.
Give your answer in 8-bit binary form.
You must show your working.

> Remember to show any digits that you have to carry during the addition.

| 0 | 1 | 0 | 1 | 0 | 1 | 1 | 1 |
|---|---|---|---|---|---|---|---|
| 0 | 1 | 0 | 1 | 1 | 1 | 1 | 1 |

**(2 marks)**

**3** (a) Add the following 8-bit binary numbers. Give your answer in 8-bit binary form.
You must show your working.

| 1 | 1 | 0 | 0 | 1 | 0 | 1 | 1 |
|---|---|---|---|---|---|---|---|
| 1 | 0 | 0 | 1 | 0 | 1 | 1 | 1 |

**(2 marks)**

(b) (i) Identify the problem that this addition has created.

.................................................................................................................... **(1 mark)**

(ii) Explain why the error has occurred.

....................................................................................................................

....................................................................................................................

....................................................................................................................

.................................................................................................................... **(2 marks)**

**4** A student was asked to add the 8-bit binary numbers, 01010111 and 01001010.
Their answer was 10110001.

Was their answer correct or incorrect? Show working to explain how you know.

....................................................................................................................

....................................................................................................................

....................................................................................................................

.................................................................................................................... **(3 marks)**

# Binary shifts

**1** (a) Explain what is meant by a binary shift.

> You are being asked to 'explain', so you should give a detailed answer with at least two items of information.

........................................................................................................................................

........................................................................................................................................

........................................................................................................................................

........................................................................................................................................ **(2 marks)**

(b) Complete a 2 place left shift on the binary number 10101011.

> Remember to move the digits two places to the left and replace the ones at the right with zeros.

........................................................................................................................................ **(1 mark)**

**2** (a) State the effect of performing a 2 place right shift on a binary number.

........................................................................................................................................

........................................................................................................................................ **(1 mark)**

(b) Complete the following table to show the effect of performing a 2 place right shift on the binary number 10101101 and the decimal (denary) equivalents of the number (dividend) and the result (quotient).

> You must carry out the shift and also convert the numbers to decimal. This will help you to check that you have carried out the shift correctly.

| Binary number (dividend) | 10101101 | Decimal equivalent | |
|---|---|---|---|
| Binary number after a 2 place right shift (quotient) | | Decimal equivalent | |

**(3 marks)**

(c) Explain the results shown in the table.

> You should state the divisor being used in a 2 place shift and any difference between the actual result and what would be expected if that divisor were used on the decimal number.

........................................................................................................................................

........................................................................................................................................

........................................................................................................................................

........................................................................................................................................ **(2 marks)**

# Hexadecimal and denary

1  (a)  Convert the hexadecimal number 9C into a decimal (denary) number.
        You must show your working.

        ..........................................................................................................................................................

        ..........................................................................................................................................................

        ..........................................................................................................................................................

        ..........................................................................................................................................  **(2 marks)**

   (b)  Convert the decimal number 249 into a hexadecimal number.
        You must show your working.

        ..........................................................................................................................................................

        ..........................................................................................................................................................

        ..........................................................................................................................................................

        ..........................................................................................................................................  **(2 marks)**

2  Write a sub-program that takes a 2-digit hexadecimal number as a parameter and
   returns the corresponding decimal number.

   > The sub-program should examine both digits of the hexadecimal number and convert any
   > letters (A–F) to decimal numbers.

   ..........................................................................................................................................................

   ..........................................................................................................................................................

   ..........................................................................................................................................................

   ..........................................................................................................................................................

   ..........................................................................................................................................................

   ..........................................................................................................................................................

   ..........................................................................................................................................................

   ..........................................................................................................................................................

   ..........................................................................................................................................................

   ..........................................................................................................................................................

   ..........................................................................................................................................................

   ..........................................................................................................................................................

   ..........................................................................................................................................................

   ..........................................................................................................................................................

   ..........................................................................................................................................  **(6 marks)**

# Hexadecimal and binary

**1** (a) Explain why hexadecimal numbers are sometimes used to represent values stored in computers, even though computers do not use hexadecimal numbers.

.....................................................................................................................................

.....................................................................................................................................

.....................................................................................................................................

..................................................................................................................... **(2 marks)**

(b) Convert the hexadecimal number C3 into an 8-bit binary number.
You must show your working.

> Remember to first convert the two digits into decimal (denary) numbers if they are letters. These can then be converted into the two nibbles of the binary number.

.....................................................................................................................................

.....................................................................................................................................

.....................................................................................................................................

.....................................................................................................................................

.....................................................................................................................................

.....................................................................................................................................

.....................................................................................................................................

.....................................................................................................................................

.....................................................................................................................................

.....................................................................................................................................

..................................................................................................................... **(3 marks)**

(c) Convert the 8-bit binary numbers 11010101 and 10111101 into hexadecimal numbers.
You must show your working.

> Remember to first convert the 8-bit number to nibbles and then convert each of these into a decimal number.

11010101

.....................................................................................................................................

.....................................................................................................................................

.....................................................................................................................................

..................................................................................................................... **(2 marks)**

10111101

.....................................................................................................................................

.....................................................................................................................................

.....................................................................................................................................

..................................................................................................................... **(2 marks)**

# Check digits

1   (a)   State the function of a check digit.

...................................................................................................................................

...................................................................................................................................   **(1 mark)**

(b)   The Eastern Bank uses accounts with five numbers which include the check digit. The fifth number is a modulus 11 check digit.
Calculate the check digit needed to complete the account number if 6389 are the first four digits.
You must show your working.

...................................................................................................................................

...................................................................................................................................

...................................................................................................................................

...................................................................................................................................

...................................................................................................................................

...................................................................................................................................

...................................................................................................................................

...................................................................................................................................   **(4 marks)**

(c)   Write an algorithm that allows a user to input a 5-digit account number and then determines whether it is valid.

> The algorithm will have to multiply each number by the weighting and find the total. Don't forget about the arithmetic operator to find the remainder of a division.

...................................................................................................................................

...................................................................................................................................

...................................................................................................................................

...................................................................................................................................

...................................................................................................................................

...................................................................................................................................

...................................................................................................................................

...................................................................................................................................

...................................................................................................................................

...................................................................................................................................

...................................................................................................................................

...................................................................................................................................   **(8 marks)**

# Characters

**1** (a) Explain what is meant by the character set of a computer.

...................................................................................................................

...................................................................................................................

................................................................................................................... **(2 marks)**

(b) Explain how ASCII is used to represent text in a computer system.

> You should say how many bits are used in the ASCII code and how many characters and actions can be represented.

...................................................................................................................

...................................................................................................................

...................................................................................................................

...................................................................................................................

...................................................................................................................

................................................................................................................... **(3 marks)**

(c) Unicode can be used to represent text in a computer system.
Explain the difference between the character sets of Unicode and ASCII.

...................................................................................................................

...................................................................................................................

................................................................................................................... **(2 marks)**

**2** Write a sub-program that takes in an item of text as a parameter and returns a string containing the ASCII codes of the characters in the text separated by spaces.

> Check the OCR pseudocode guide for the command to return the ASCII code for a character.
> This question will help you to develop your problem-solving and programming skills.

...................................................................................................................

...................................................................................................................

...................................................................................................................

...................................................................................................................

...................................................................................................................

...................................................................................................................

...................................................................................................................

...................................................................................................................

................................................................................................................... **(6 marks)**

# Images

1   Figure 1 is a bitmap image.

Figure 1

(a)   State what is meant by the following terms.

The size of an image

........................................................................................................................

........................................................................................................................

The resolution of an image

........................................................................................................................

........................................................................................................................ **(2 marks)**

(b)   The number of colours represented in an image depends on the colour depth used. Complete the table to show the number of colours that can be represented using the following colour depths.

| Colour depth | Number of colours represented |
|:---:|---|
| 1 | |
| 3 | |
| 8 | |

**(3 marks)**

(c)   The image in Figure 1 has the following properties: width = 2000; height = 3000; colour depth = 24.
Calculate the file size of this image in megabytes. You must show your working.

........................................................................................................................

........................................................................................................................

........................................................................................................................

........................................................................................................................ **(3 marks)**

(d)   Image files can contain metadata. Explain, giving examples, what is meant by 'metadata'.

> The question states 'giving examples' and so you will need more than one.

........................................................................................................................

........................................................................................................................

........................................................................................................................

........................................................................................................................ **(2 marks)**

# Sound

**1** Sound can be represented digitally by taking samples of the original sound.

   (a)  (i)  State what is meant by sampling frequency.

......................................................................................................................

...................................................................................................................... **(1 mark)**

       (ii)  Describe the effect of increasing the sampling frequency.

......................................................................................................................

......................................................................................................................

......................................................................................................................

...................................................................................................................... **(2 marks)**

   (b)  Define what is meant by the 'bit rate' of a recording and explain how it can be calculated.

> Don't confuse the terms 'bit depth' and 'bit rate'.

......................................................................................................................

......................................................................................................................

......................................................................................................................

......................................................................................................................

......................................................................................................................

...................................................................................................................... **(3 marks)**

   (c)  (i)  Kerry is experimenting with different sampling frequencies.
Calculate the bit rate of a recording if she chooses a sampling frequency of 50 kHz if 16 bits are used to encode each sample.

> Remember to convert kHz to Hz for the calculation.

......................................................................................................................

......................................................................................................................

...................................................................................................................... **(2 marks)**

       (ii)  Calculate the file size, in megabytes, of a 100-second recording with a sampling frequency of 44.1 kHz if 16 bits are used to encode each sample.

> You should always show your working in questions involving calculations. You may get some credit for showing that you understand the method even if your final answer is wrong.

......................................................................................................................

......................................................................................................................

......................................................................................................................

...................................................................................................................... **(3 marks)**

# Compression

**1** Leah is sending files to her brother Ollie, while he is away on holiday, by attaching them to emails. The files include images, music, and PDF and word processed documents.

(a) Identify **two** advantages for Leah and Ollie of compressing the files.

1 ..............................................................................................................................

..............................................................................................................................

2 ..............................................................................................................................

..............................................................................................................................  **(2 marks)**

(b) Two types of compression are lossless and lossy.
Describe the difference between lossless and lossy compression.

..............................................................................................................................

..............................................................................................................................

..............................................................................................................................

..............................................................................................................................

..............................................................................................................................

..............................................................................................................................

..............................................................................................................................

..............................................................................................................................  **(4 marks)**

(c) State which type of compression is appropriate for each of the following files that Leah sends and explain why it is appropriate.

**A PDF file of a novel.**
Type of compression

..............................................................................................................................

Reason

..............................................................................................................................

..............................................................................................................................

**Images of her trip to London.**
Type of compression

..............................................................................................................................

Reason

..............................................................................................................................

..............................................................................................................................

..............................................................................................................................  **(4 marks)**

# Computational thinking, algorithms and programming

1  (a)  (i)  Add together the following two 8-bit binary numbers.

1　0　1　1　1　0　1　1
0　1　1　0　1　0　1　0

**(2 marks)**

　　　(ii)  State the name of the error that has occurred when adding these two binary numbers.

...................................................................................................................................

...................................................................................................................................　**(1 mark)**

　(b)  Convert the binary number 10111011 to decimal, showing your working.

...................................................................................................................................

...................................................................................................................................

...................................................................................................................................

...................................................................................................................................　**(2 marks)**

　(c)  (i)  Convert the binary number 11110111 to hexadecimal.

...................................................................................................................................

...................................................................................................................................

...................................................................................................................................

...................................................................................................................................　**(2 marks)**

　　　(ii)  Explain why programmers prefer to use hexadecimal.

...................................................................................................................................

...................................................................................................................................

...................................................................................................................................

...................................................................................................................................　**(2 marks)**

　(d)  Explain why data is stored in computers in a binary format.

...................................................................................................................................

...................................................................................................................................

...................................................................................................................................

...................................................................................................................................　**(2 marks)**

2 Figure 1 is a bitmap image that Ann took with her camera during her trip to the seaside and downloaded to her laptop.

Figure 1

(a) The operating system gives the properties of the image as having a width of 5000 and a height of 4000 and a colour depth of 24.

(i) State the units in which the width and height are measured.

.................................................................................................................................... **(1 mark)**

(ii) Explain what is meant by 'colour depth'.

....................................................................................................................................

....................................................................................................................................

....................................................................................................................................

.................................................................................................................................... **(2 marks)**

(iii) Calculate the file size of the image in megabytes.
You must show your working.

....................................................................................................................................

....................................................................................................................................

....................................................................................................................................

.................................................................................................................................... **(2 marks)**

(b) When Ann inserted the image into a document and enlarged it to fill a full page, she was disappointed by the quality, as shown in Figure 2.

Explain why the quality was affected by enlarging the image.

Figure 2

....................................................................................................................................

....................................................................................................................................

....................................................................................................................................

.................................................................................................................................... **(2 marks)**

(c) The operating system also gave Ann information about the date and time when the image was taken.

(i) State what this type of information is called.

.................................................................................................................................... **(1 mark)**

(ii) State **two** other items of information you would expect to be stored with the image.

Item 1

.................................................................................................................

Item 2

................................................................................................................. **(2 marks)**

(d) Lossy compression algorithms are often used to reduce the file size of image files.

(i) Explain what is meant by 'lossy compression'.

.................................................................................................................

.................................................................................................................

.................................................................................................................

................................................................................................................. **(2 marks)**

(ii) Explain why these algorithms are suitable for image files but should not be used to reduce the size of text files.

.................................................................................................................

.................................................................................................................

.................................................................................................................

................................................................................................................. **(2 marks)**

3   Stephen has stored the names of the countries he has visited in an array named 'countries'. Part of the data is shown in Figure 3.

Figure 3

| Peru | Laos | Cambodia | India | Australia | Nepal |
|------|------|----------|-------|-----------|-------|

(a) Explain why an array is a suitable data structure to store this data.

.................................................................................................................

.................................................................................................................

.................................................................................................................

................................................................................................................. **(2 marks)**

(b) Show the stages of a bubble sort algorithm when applied to data shown in Figure 3.

.................................................................................................................

.................................................................................................................

.................................................................................................................

.................................................................................................................

.................................................................................................................

................................................................................................................. **(4 marks)**

(c) Write an algorithm, in pseudocode, that would allow a user to search the array for any country they enter. The algorithm should stop if the country is found and notify the user whether the search has been successful or not.

......................................................................................................................................

......................................................................................................................................

......................................................................................................................................

......................................................................................................................................

......................................................................................................................................

......................................................................................................................................

......................................................................................................................................

......................................................................................................................................

......................................................................................................................................

......................................................................................................................................

......................................................................................................................................

......................................................................................................................................

......................................................................................................................................

......................................................................................................................................

......................................................................................................................................

......................................................................................................................................

......................................................................................................................................

......................................................................................................................................

......................................................................................................................................

......................................................................................................................................

......................................................................................................................... **(6 marks)**

(d) Stephen would like to store the country data in the array in a text file.
Write an algorithm, in pseudocode, that would allow him to do that.

......................................................................................................................................

......................................................................................................................................

......................................................................................................................................

......................................................................................................................................

......................................................................................................................................

......................................................................................................................... **(4 marks)**

**4** (a)  Complete a 2 place right shift on the binary number 11101010.

........................................................................................................................................

........................................................................................................ **(1 mark)**

(b)  Complete a 2 place left shift on the binary number 00010101.

........................................................................................................................................

........................................................................................................ **(1 mark)**

(c)  Divide 11001010 by 8.

........................................................................................................................................

........................................................................................................ **(1 mark)**

**5** (a)  Complete the truth table for the logic diagram shown in Figure 4.

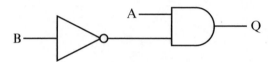

Figure 4

| A | B | Q |
|---|---|---|
| 0 | 0 | 0 |
| 0 | 1 |   |
| 1 | 0 |   |
| 1 | 1 |   |

**(3 marks)**

(b)  Draw a logic diagram and complete the truth table for the following equation
P = NOT(A OR B).

Logic diagram

Truth table

| A | B | P |
|---|---|---|
| 0 | 0 |   |
| 0 | 1 |   |
| 1 | 0 |   |
| 1 | 1 |   |

**(4 marks)**

**6** Leah has designed this algorithm to convert any measurement made in centimetres to inches and vice versa.

```
01  choice = input("Which units are you entering? Enter 'I' for inches
    and 'C' for centimetres.")
02  valueToConvert = int(input("Please enter the measurement as a whole
    number."))
03  if choice == "I" then
04      conversion = valueToConvert * 0.39
05  else
06      conversion = valueToConvert * 2.54
07  endif
08  print(conversion)
```

(a) Leah is using an integrated development environment (IDE) to create the program. Describe **two** tools in an IDE that can help Leah to develop the program.

1 ...........................................................................................................................................

..............................................................................................................................................

..............................................................................................................................................

..............................................................................................................................................

2 ...........................................................................................................................................

..............................................................................................................................................

..............................................................................................................................................

.......................................................................................................................... **(4 marks)**

(b) The variable valueToConvert has been typecast as data type integer. Identify **two** other variables and state the data type of each.

1 ...........................................................................................................................................

Data type .............................................................................................................................

2 ...........................................................................................................................................

Data type .......................................................................................................... **(4 marks)**

(c) When Leah asks her friends to test the program it will carry out a calculation even if an entry other than 'I' or 'C' is made. Edit the algorithm by adding lines before 02 to authenticate the user entry for the units they wish to convert.

..............................................................................................................................................

..............................................................................................................................................

..............................................................................................................................................

..............................................................................................................................................

..............................................................................................................................................

..............................................................................................................................................

..............................................................................................................................................

.................................................................................................................................

.................................................................................................................................

.................................................................................................................................

.................................................................................................................................

.................................................................................................................................   **(6 marks)**

7  Figure 5 shows a flow diagram of the printing of a parking ticket at a pay and display car park.

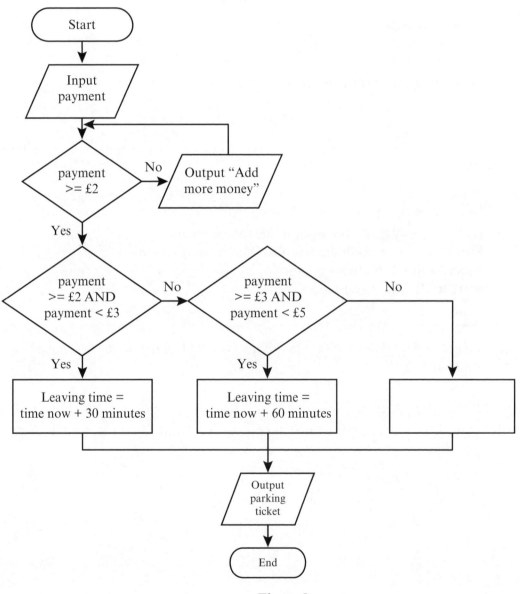

Figure 5

(a) (i)  State the minimum amount that car park users must pay.

.................................................................................................................................

(ii) State how long a user can park if they pay £3.50.

.................................................................................................................................   **(2 marks)**

(b) If users pay £5 they can park for the whole day. Complete the flow diagram by writing in the empty symbols.        **(4 marks)**

8   A grocery shop records details of their stock in a database table named 'Products', as shown in Figure 6.

| ProductID | Name | Supplier | ReorderLevel | NumberInStock |
|-----------|------|----------|--------------|---------------|
| 0001 | Crisps | Smith and Co | 30 | 120 |
| 0002 | Peas | Jacob's | 20 | 30 |
| 0003 | Baked beans | Smith and Co | 50 | 60 |
| 0004 | Tinned tomatoes | Smith and Co | 50 | 60 |
| 0005 | Peas | Smith and Co | 20 | 30 |
| 0006 | Peaches | Jacob's | 10 | 20 |
| 0007 | Frozen chips | Jacob's | 50 | 90 |

Figure 6

(a) (i)  State the key field for this table.

.......................................................................................................................... **(1 mark)**

(ii) Explain why this will be the key field.

..............................................................................................................................

..............................................................................................................................

..............................................................................................................................

.......................................................................................................................... **(2 marks)**

(b) Here is a query that is run against this database table.
State how many records are returned from running this query.
Select * FROM Products
WHERE ReorderLevel >= 30;

.......................................................................................................................... **(1 mark)**

(c) Complete the WHERE clause in this query to find all the products supplied by Smith and Co.
SELECT * FROM Products
WHERE                                                                              **(2 marks)**

(d) Write down the SQL (structured query language) commands that would return the following records.

| Peas | Jacob's | 20 |
|------|---------|----|
| Peaches | Jacob's | 10 |

.........................................................................................................................

.........................................................................................................................

.........................................................................................................................

.........................................................................................................................

.........................................................................................................................

.........................................................................................................................

.......................................................................................................................... **(3 marks)**

# Computer systems

1   Jamila has just bought a new laptop.
The laptop was advertised as having a 2.6 GHz quad core CPU with a 6 megabyte cache and 16 gigabytes of RAM.

(a)   The role of the CPU is to process program instructions using the fetch–execute cycle.
Complete the following table to explain the functions of the components of the CPU in this cycle.

| Component | Function |
|---|---|
| CU (Control Unit) | |
| Program counter | |
| MAR (Memory Address Register) | |
| MDR (Memory Data Register) | |
| ALU (Arithmetic Logic Unit) | |

**(5 marks)**

(b)   The laptop has a quad core processor. The salesman told Jamila that this would be faster than a single core processor because it could perform parallel processing and multitasking.
Explain what is meant by:

Parallel processing

.......................................................................................................................

.......................................................................................................................

.......................................................................................................................

.......................................................................................................................

Multitasking

.......................................................................................................................

.......................................................................................................................

.......................................................................................................................

....................................................................................................... **(4 marks)**

(c)  The CPU has a 6 megabyte cache.
Explain how the cache improves the performance of the processor.

.......................................................................................................................................

.......................................................................................................................................

.......................................................................................................................................

.......................................................................................................................................  **(2 marks)**

(d)  The salesman told Jamila that because the laptop had 16 gigabytes of RAM it
would not have to make use of virtual memory.
Explain what is meant by virtual memory and why it is needed.

.......................................................................................................................................

.......................................................................................................................................

.......................................................................................................................................

.......................................................................................................................................  **(2 marks)**

(e)  In addition to RAM, the laptop's memory also contains ROM.
Tick **one** box in each row of the table below to show whether each of the
statements is true for ROM or RAM.

| | RAM | ROM |
|---|---|---|
| Program instructions and data are stored here. | | |
| It is used to boot up the laptop when it is switched on. | | |
| It is volatile. | | |

**(3 marks)**

2   A team of programmers is developing an online game that can be played on different
devices including computers, tablets and smartphones. The program is being written
in a high-level language, which will be translated into machine code.

(a)  Describe what is meant by machine code.

.......................................................................................................................................

.......................................................................................................................................

.......................................................................................................................................

.......................................................................................................................................  **(2 marks)**

(b)  Describe what is meant by a high-level language.

.......................................................................................................................................

.......................................................................................................................................

.......................................................................................................................................

.......................................................................................................................................  **(2 marks)**

(c) Explain **two** advantages to the team of using a high-level language to develop the game.

1 ...............................................................................................................................

.................................................................................................................................

.................................................................................................................................

.................................................................................................................................

2 ...............................................................................................................................

.................................................................................................................................

.................................................................................................................................

................................................................................................................................. **(4 marks)**

3  Computer systems usually include secondary storage devices.

(a)  Explain why secondary storage devices are needed.

.................................................................................................................................

.................................................................................................................................

.................................................................................................................................

................................................................................................................................. **(2 marks)**

(b)  Complete the table below to show whether magnetic, optical or solid state storage is most appropriate for each situation. Give a reason in each case.

| Situation | Magnetic, optical or solid state | Reason why this is the most appropriate |
|---|---|---|
| Storing images, videos and music in a hand held device. | | |
| Data storage in the file servers of a large network. | | |
| Storing programs, images and videos to be given away free with a computer magazine. | | |

**(6 marks)**

4  Jack thinks that his computer may have malware.

(a)  Explain what is meant by 'malware'.

.................................................................................................................................

.................................................................................................................................

.................................................................................................................................

................................................................................................................................. **(2 marks)**

(b)  Describe **two** types of malware.

Type 1 ...........................................................................................................................

...........................................................................................................................

...........................................................................................................................

...........................................................................................................................

Type 2 ...........................................................................................................................

...........................................................................................................................

...........................................................................................................................

........................................................................................................... **(4 marks)**

(c)  State **two** precautions that Jack should take to prevent infection by malware.

Precaution 1 ...................................................................................................................

...........................................................................................................................

Precaution 2 ...................................................................................................................

........................................................................................................... **(2 marks)**

5  A design company with 100 employees has decided to install a network to improve
communications and productivity.
They have decided to use a client–server network with a star topology.

(a)  Draw and label a diagram to show how the computers and any required
equipment could be connected using a star topology.

**(3 marks)**

(b)  Describe **two** roles of a server in a client–server network.

Role 1 ...........................................................................................................................

...........................................................................................................................

...........................................................................................................................

...........................................................................................................................

Role 2 ..................................................................................................................

.........................................................................................................................

.........................................................................................................................

......................................................................................................... **(4 marks)**

(c)  When computers communicate with each other on a network they must use the same protocol.
Define 'protocol'.

.........................................................................................................................

.........................................................................................................................

.........................................................................................................................

......................................................................................................... **(2 marks)**

(d)  The table below lists the names of the layers in which the protocols are arranged.

   (i)  Number the empty cells to indicate the order in which data will pass when it is being transmitted by a computer. The first one has been done for you.

Guided

| Layer | Order |
|-------|-------|
| Transport layer | |
| Network access layer | |
| Application layer | 1 |
| Internet layer | |

**(3 marks)**

   (ii)  Describe **two** advantages to computer scientists of organising the protocols into layers.

Advantage 1 ..........................................................................................

.........................................................................................................................

.........................................................................................................................

.........................................................................................................................

Advantage 2 ..........................................................................................

.........................................................................................................................

.........................................................................................................................

......................................................................................................... **(4 marks)**

(e) Describe the security measures and network policies that should be used to safeguard the security and privacy of the company's data on the network.

..........................................................................................................................................

..........................................................................................................................................

..........................................................................................................................................

..........................................................................................................................................

..........................................................................................................................................

..........................................................................................................................................

..........................................................................................................................................

..........................................................................................................................................

..........................................................................................................................................

..........................................................................................................................................

..........................................................................................................................................

..........................................................................................................................................

..........................................................................................................................................

..........................................................................................................................................

..........................................................................................................................................

.................................................................................................................... **(8 marks)**

6 Legislation governing the use of computer science technology includes the following acts:

A The Data Protection Act 1998

B Computer Misuse Act 1990

C Copyright, Designs and Patents Act 1988

State which legislation applies to each of the following actions by writing one of the letters A, B or C.

(a) Accessing another user's files without their permission.

..........................................................................................................................................

(b) Downloading and using images without their creators' permission.

..........................................................................................................................................

(c) Storing more personal data about a user than is required.

..........................................................................................................................................

(d) Making a copy of a chart topping music CD for your personal use.

.................................................................................................................... **(4 marks)**

7  A school is considering changing from using proprietary to open-source software on its network.

(a)  Describe what is meant by proprietary and open-source software.

Proprietary software

.............................................................................................................................

.............................................................................................................................

.............................................................................................................................

.............................................................................................................................

Open-source software

.............................................................................................................................

.............................................................................................................................

.............................................................................................................................

.............................................................................................................  **(4 marks)**

(b)  Describe **two** benefits for the school and the students of using proprietary software.

Benefit 1

.............................................................................................................................

.............................................................................................................................

.............................................................................................................................

Benefit 2

.............................................................................................................................

.............................................................................................................................

.............................................................................................................  **(4 marks)**

(c)  State **two** benefits to the school and the students of using open-source software.

Benefit 1

.............................................................................................................................

.............................................................................................................................

.............................................................................................................................

Benefit 2

.............................................................................................................................

.............................................................................................................................

.............................................................................................................  **(4 marks)**

# Answers

## SYSTEM ARCHITECTURE

### 1. The central processing unit

1

| Component of CPU | Function |
|---|---|
| CU (control unit) | Controls the other components of the CPU. |
| Clock | Controls the rate at which program instructions are carried out. |
| ALU (arithmetic logic unit) | Performs arithmetic and logical operations to carry out program instructions. |
| Cache | Stores frequently used program instructions and data so the processor isn't kept waiting for them to be transferred from the main memory. |
| Registers | Memory locations. Some perform special functions in the fetch–decode–execute cycle. |

2 A laptop with a 3 GHz CPU could have a better performance as it has a higher clock speed. This means that it will process program instructions more quickly than a computer with a 2 GHz processor, so programs will run faster.
However, the 2 GHz computer could have more cache memory to store frequently used instructions. It could also have a greater number of cores, which improve performance by allowing multitasking and parallel processing.
The 2 GHz computer could also have more RAM, which would improve performance because the CPU would not have to use virtual memory.

### 2. Components of the CPU

1 1 Memory to store program data and instructions.
  2 Input and output devices (for example, a secondary storage device such as a magnetic hard drive).
2 The CU coordinates the actions of the computer. It sends out control signals to other parts of the CPU and to other components of the computer.
The ALU performs arithmetic and logical operations. It carries out activities such as:
  • addition, subtraction, multiplication and division
  • comparisons between two different numbers.
3 The MDR is a temporary store (buffer) for anything copied from memory.
The accumulator is a temporary store for the results of calculations carried out by the ALU.

### 3. Fetch–decode–execute cycle 1

1 (a) Any two from:
     • memory to store program data and instructions
     • input and output devices (could include secondary storage devices, keyboard, mouse, printer, loudspeaker etc).
  (b) A computer in which the program instructions and the data are stored in memory.

2 (a)

| Description | Order |
|---|---|
| The next instruction is sent from the RAM to the CPU. | 2 |
| The instruction is carried out. | 4 |
| The CU interprets the instruction. | 3 |
| The CPU sends a signal to the RAM requesting the next instruction. | 1 |

(b) RAM is where the program instructions and data are stored until they are needed.

(c)

| CU (control unit) | | ALU (arithmetic logic unit) |
|---|---|---|
| The CU **decodes** the instructions. If a calculation is needed, the CU instructs the **ALU**. | ▶ | **Calculations** are carried out in the ALU. |

### 4. Fetch–execute–decode cycle 2

1 A register is a memory location within the CPU used to store program instructions and/or data. Some registers perform special functions in the fetch-decode-execute cycle.

2 (a)

| Program Counter | 2 |
|---|---|
| MAR | 1 |
| MDR | ADD 4 |
| Accumulator | 12 |

(b)

| Program Counter | 3 |
|---|---|
| MAR | 2 |
| MDR | STORE 5 |
| Accumulator | 12 |

(c) The value 9 is stored in the accumulator and 3 is added to it to give 12. This value is then stored in memory location 5.

### 5. Performance of the CPU

1 The cache consists of very fast memory and it is used to store frequently used commands and data. These can be accessed more quickly from the cache than from the slower RAM when they are needed.
2 (a) A multi-core processor.
  (b) Multi-core processors improve performance as they have two CPUs which can work together on the same program (parallel processing) or work on different ones (multitasking).
  (c) Performance cannot be improved indefinitely because the rate at which the transistors process the instructions is limited. There can also be a problem with the amount of heat generated by high clock speeds, which may cause a malfunction if it cannot be dissipated.
3 Too expensive.
4 In sequential programs, one task requires the output of a previous task, so the second task cannot start until the first task has finished.

### 6. Embedded systems

1 (a) An embedded system is a computer system built into another device in order to control it.
  (b) For example: Processor, memory, input and output interfaces.
  (c) Examples of devices that have embedded systems include: washing machine, microwave oven, television, camera.
2 (a) Desktop computers are designed to run a range of different applications e.g. word processors, spreadsheets, DVD players, games, while each embedded system is designed to perform a small, specific range of functions linked to the device it is embedded into.
  (b) Embedded systems are described as real-time systems because they must guarantee a response almost immediately in order for the system to react to different situations.
  (c) Assembly language is used so that the hardware can be directly controlled by the programs written. This is far more efficient than using a high-level language that needs an interpreter or compiler.

## MEMORY

### 7. RAM and ROM

1 (a) Volatile memory provides temporary storage for program instructions and data. It loses its content when the electrical power is switched off.

 (b) Non-volatile memory is used for instructions that do not need to be changed in normal use. For example, the sets of instructions needed for a computer to start are stored in ROM.

2

| Statement | True |
|---|---|
| RAM stands for Random Access Memory | ✓ |
| ROM is volatile | |
| Data can be read from and written to ROM | |
| Program instructions and data are stored in RAM | ✓ |
| The sets of instructions needed for a computer to start are stored in ROM | ✓ |

3 RAM is volatile but ROM is non-volatile.
RAM can be written to and read from, but ROM can only be read from.
RAM stores program instructions and data, but ROM is used to store the sets of instructions needed for a computer to start.

4 One from:
Sets of instructions needed for the computer to start. Data used by a program when it is executing.

### 8. Virtual memory

1 (a) Virtual memory is an area of the hard disk drive or solid-state drive used as temporary RAM when the actual RAM is full. Instructions that haven't been used recently are swapped out to virtual memory to free up space in main memory for other instructions and data that the processor needs immediately.

 (b) When a computer is running the operating system and several applications at the same time, the random access memory (RAM) often becomes full. The operating system will use virtual memory to store some of the data, usually on the hard disk drive.

 (c) If there is no free memory, the operating system will 'swap out' some of the data stored in RAM to the swap area on the hard disk drive and 'swap in' the requested data to the now free area. Usually the least recently used stored data is swapped out and, if it is needed again, it is then swapped back in at the expense of other data.

2 (a) By using virtual memory, the computer will be able to continue to process instructions without having to close down any programs. There will be a significant drop in performance if the computer system relies too heavily on using virtual memory because the read/write speed of a magnetic disk drive is a lot slower than that of RAM.

 (b) He could add more RAM. This would improve performance as the operating system would not have to make so much use of virtual memory.

## SECONDARY STORAGE

### 9. Secondary storage 1: optical and magnetic devices

1 (a) 1 Data that is stored in RAM is lost when the power is turned off because RAM is volatile.
 2 A secondary storage device, such as a hard drive, provides permanent storage for data that would otherwise be lost when the power is turned off.
 You could also include:
 Data can be moved between computers using secondary storage devices.

 (b) (i) Magnetic storage devices use electromagnets in their read/write heads to read and write the data, which is encoded as opposing magnetic polarities on the surface of the disk or tape.

 (ii) Optical disks use a laser to read and write data. The data is encoded as a series of pits in a spiral track running from the inside to the outside of the disk.

 (c) Data can be written to and read from magnetic devices far more rapidly than from optical devices. This improves the performance of the data processing.

2 200 photos at 8 MB each needs a total of $200 \times 8$ MB = 1600 MB = 1.6 GB.
A single CD can store 700 MB, so Noah's photos cannot be saved on a single CD.
A single DVD can store 4.7 GB, so his photos can be saved on a single DVD.

### 10. Secondary storage 2: solid-state memory

1 (a) 1 GB = 1000 MB
 6 GB = $6 \times 1000$ = 6000 MB

 (b) (i) It is called a solid-state storage device because it has no moving parts.
 (ii) For example: Solid-state drives; USB drives.
 (iii) Any two from:
 Lighter and more portable. No moving parts that can be damaged if dropped. Data access speeds are faster than for magnetic storage.

 (c) Solid-state memory is made of flash memory uses arrays of transistors working as switches that are set to represent the digits 1 or 0. These retain their state when the power is switched off.

### 11. Storage 3: capacity, speed and cost

Your answer should include comparisons of the following:
**Capacity**: At the present time, magnetic storage devices have the highest capacity, commonly 1 to 2 TB in home computers. Solid-state drives are becoming larger and laptops often have drives of 500 GB to 1 TB.
**Speed**: Solid-state devices are very fast compared with magnetic devices. Magnetic disks can access data in milliseconds (thousandths of a second). Solid-state devices can access data in fractions of milliseconds.
**Portability**: Both types of storage device are portable. Hard disk drives are more susceptible to knocks because of the read/write heads. Solid-state devices are more portable because they are small and light and have no moving parts.
**Durability**: Magnetic storage devices are very durable and can be written to an infinite number of times. Solid-state devices are less durable than hard disk drives and have a limited number of erase/write cycles.
**Reliability**: Magnetic storage devices are very reliable for short- and long-term storage. Damage may occur if the read/write heads knock against the disk platters. Solid-state devices are very reliable. There are no moving parts and they are unaffected by magnetic fields.
**Cost**: At the present time, the cost of magnetic and optical data storage is very low per byte. The cost is higher for solid-state devices but the price is falling rapidly as they become more common.

### 12. Storage 4: portability, durability and reliability

1 (a) (i) Solid-state storage.
 (ii) Solid-state storage has no moving parts so it is very portable, which makes it suitable for devices such as laptops which are carried around.
 It is also very light which makes it suitable for portable devices.

 (b) 1 DVDs are very cheap and store up to 4.7 GB of data.
 2 DVDs are very light and easy to distribute.

 (c) Optical.

 (d) The solid-state drive can be accessed more rapidly and used for system files, programs and application data that need to be accessed rapidly and frequently.
 The slower, hard disk drive can be used for long-term storage of files that don't need to be accessed as quickly.

## WIRED AND WIRELESS NETWORKS

### 13. Networks 1: LANs and WANs

1  (a) A network is a group of computer systems and devices linked together so that they can communicate and share resources.

   (b) 1  The users can share resources such as printers and internet connections.

   2  Files can be shared by users across the network and they can work collaboratively.

2  A LAN is a network in a small area such as a home, school, office building or group of buildings on a single site.
   A LAN is usually managed by a local manager or team at the site.
   It is owned by the organisation that uses it.
   A WAN connects separate LANs over a large geographical area to form a network of networks. The internet is a WAN.
   Computers in a WAN can communicate with computers and users in other locations.
   A WAN is managed by several different people or parts of an organisation working together.

### 14. Networks 2: client–server and peer-to-peer

1  (a) In peer-to-peer networks, there is only one type of computer and there is no server to manage the network. All the computers are equal and they can communicate with each other directly without having to go through a server.
   Each user can give other users access to their computer and their programs and to any devices such as printers attached to them.

   (b) Any two from:
   • Expensive server and network operating systems are not required, so it is cheaper.
   • Specialist staff are not required to administer and maintain the network, which saves money.
   • A peer-to-peer network is much easier and requires less specialist knowledge to set up.

   (c) 1  All data can be saved on the file server, so it can all be backed up at the same time without having to back up the data on each computer separately.

   2  Network security is stronger because access to file servers is controlled centrally using login names and passwords.

### 15. Transmission media

1  (a) Data is transmitted along copper cables as electric signals.
   In fibre optic cables, data are transmitted as pulses of light generated by a light emitting diode (LED) or a laser.

   (b) Advantage: Signals are transmitted over longer distances and at faster speeds.
   Disadvantage: More expensive than copper cable.

2  (a) Radio waves are used to transmit data across networks using frequencies of between 2.4 and 5 GHz.

   (b) Each frequency range is divided into separate channels. For example, in the 2.4 GHz range used by most networks, there are 14 channels spaced 5 MHz apart. Users can change the operating channel of their Wi-Fi device to prevent interference.

3  (a) Security is good in a cable network as each computer has to be physically plugged into the network using a cable.
   Security is poor in a wireless network as anyone within range could log into the network.

   (b) There is no interference in a cable network as the cables through which the data is transmitted can be shielded.
   In a wireless network, signals can be affected by other electronic equipment and obstacles such as walls.

   (c) In a cable network bandwidth is high – up to 10 Gbps. In a wireless network bandwidth is lower – up to 600 Mbps.

### 16. Connecting computers to a LAN

1  (a) A NIC provides a physical connection to either a wired or a wireless network for a device on the network.
   The NIC formats the data so that it can be transmitted and received across the network.

   (b) Every NIC is created with its own unique **media access control (MAC)** number programmed into it.
   Because all devices on the same network have different MAC addresses it enables the senders and recipients of data to be uniquely identified.

2  A switch transmits the data to the intended recipient only, whereas a hub broadcasts it to all the devices on the network.
   Sending the data to only the expected recipient reduces the network traffic and improves the efficiency of the network.

3  (a) A wireless access point enables wireless devices to connect to cabled networks.

   (b) The router connects two networks – the home network and the internet link provided by the family's internet service provider.
   The router sends the requests from each of the home computers to internet servers and distributes the incoming data to the correct computers as identified by their IP addresses.

### 17. The internet

1  (a) (i)  Every computer accessing the internet needs its own unique address so that other computers know where to send any requested data, such as web pages, and can identify the computers communicating with them. This is provided by its IP address which uniquely identifies the computer on the internet.
      (ii) 32 bits – $4 \times 8$ bits.

   (b) When a browser requests access to a host using its domain name, the client computer contacts a DNS (domain name server). The DNS contains a database of domain names which allows it to look up the domain name and return the IP address to the computer.

2  (a) A web host is a computer that provides space for a website on a server so that it can be accessed by users at remote locations over networks, including the internet.

   (b) Any four from:
   • Ayana will have to keep her computer switched on 24 hours a day, 7 days a week.
   • She will need to have a static internet address, i.e. one that stays the same.
   • She will need a very fast broadband connection capable of handling a large number of users.
   • If a computer failure takes place, she needs the technical knowledge to repair it quickly, or she needs another computer that will instantly take over delivery of her website.
   • She will need a great deal of technical knowledge in addition to that needed to design her website.
   • She will need to be able to protect her website against threats from hackers and other unscrupulous users.

## NETWORK TOPOLOGIES, PROTOCOLS AND LAYERS

### 18. Network topologies

1  (a)

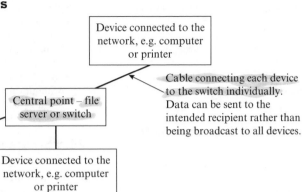

Device connected to the network, e.g. computer or printer

Central point – file server or switch

Cable connecting each device to the switch individually. Data can be sent to the intended recipient rather than being broadcast to all devices.

Device connected to the network, e.g. computer or printer

Device connected to the network, e.g. computer or printer

(b) For example:
1 Data is sent directly to only the intended computer and therefore network traffic is kept to a minimum.
2 If one link fails, all the other devices will continue to operate, as data are sent to each computer individually.
3 It is easy to add new devices without disrupting the network, as each device has its own communications cable.

### 19. Protocols 1: browsers and email clients

1  (a) Protocols are used to control:
• data formats, to ensure that data can be exchanged consistently and accurately
• address formats, to identify senders and recipients and to ensure that data goes to the right addresses
• routing, to provide the right information so that data can flow through networks correctly.

(b)

| Protocol | Function |
|---|---|
| HTTPS | This protocol is used when communications between a client and host have to be encrypted. |
| SMTP | Provides the rules for sending email messages from client to server and then from server to server until they reach their destination. |
| HTTP | Provides the rules to be followed by web browsers when accessing websites and by web servers when requesting and supplying information. |
| FTP | Provides the rules for transferring files between computers. |

(c) (i) Transmission control protocol/internet protocol
(ii) TCP divides data sent from the application layer into packets. It checks that data has been sent correctly and has been received, or notifies the sender that data has not been received.
IP adds the source and destination IP addresses to the data and routes it to the recipient computer.

### 20. Protocols 2: network layers

1  (a) Application layer: Provides an interface to applications such as web browsers and email clients.
Transport layer: Splits the data into packets and checks that they are correctly sent and received.
Network access layer: Transmits the data to the devices in the LAN.
(b) Application layer: HTTP, HTTPS, FTP, SMTP, POP, IMAP
Transport layer: TCP
Internet layer: IP

2  1 Application layer   2 Transport layer   3 Internet layer
4 Network access layer

### 21. Protocols 3: benefits of layers

1  Any three from:
• The overall model is simplified by dividing it into functional parts, so it's easier to visualise the functions.
• Different layers can be combined in different ways as required for different circumstances.
• One layer can be developed or changed without affecting the other layers, as they are separate.
• As each layer has a specific task, it is easier to identify and correct networking errors and problems.

2  (a) A virtual network is a software-based network that allows users to communicate locally and remotely as if connected to a physical network, using a consistent interface.
(b) Any two from:
• Allows users to communicate securely.
• They allow David and his colleagues to communicate and share information privately without it being visible to other users of the LAN.
• They reduce network traffic because data will be sent only to members of the VPN.
• Users can access resources anywhere around the world as though they are on a local network.
• They allow users to control one or more remotely located computers over the internet.

3  Protocols provide a universal standard for hardware and software manufacturers to follow so that their devices will be able to communicate with each other.

### 22. Packets and packet switching

1  (a) To make the data easier to transmit, as a very high bandwidth would be required for large files.
(b) (i) The data is broken down into small portions called packets.
The sender and recipient addresses are added to the packet.
Routers inspect the recipient address and direct the packets on to the correct network.
Different packets can take different routes and use different intermediate networks.
The recipient computer reassembles the packets, which may not arrive in the correct order.
(ii) Any one from: Packet switching improves data security because packets don't all take the same route to their destination, making it impossible to intercept the complete data file.
If there is a technical problem on part of the network, the packets can be directed around it.

2 Advantages include:
- Data can be accessed from any computer and from anywhere in the world.
- All of the data is automatically backed up at the remote site.

Disadvantages include:
- An internet connection is required and may not be available.
- The cloud storage site may be targeted by hackers.
- Download and upload speeds might be slow.

## SYSTEM SECURITY

### 23. Threats to networks 1: people as the weak point

Users often pose the greatest threats to networks, either through their direct actions or by allowing criminals access to the networks by the things that they do.

Network policies should cover the use of removable media such as USB flash drives, smartphones, CDs, DVDs, MP3 players and digital cameras. These devices pose a threat because they can introduce malware to the network.

If data is removed illegally, the company may be sued if this data is covered by the Data Protection Act and there is the risk of the devices being lost or stolen. Network policies may state that only devices provided by the company can be used.

Network policies should cover user authentication and the use of passwords. Network policies should ensure that users do not use passwords which are easy to remember and are based on personal details such as birth dates and the names of family members. Network policies should be used to ensure that all user passwords are at least 8 characters long and contain numbers, letters (upper and lower case) and non-alphanumeric characters such as exclamation marks. They should be changed regularly and old ones should never be reused.

Users may be susceptible to social engineering (tricking people into divulging secret information or doing things that they would not otherwise do). Social engineering techniques include:
- 'blagging', where a criminal uses a voice call or email to try to get a user to divulge information
- 'phishing', which is the use of fraudulent emails
- 'shouldering', where a user can be watched or filmed entering user names and passwords.

Network policies should ensure that users do not divulge any details and they should be given information about, and training on how to deal with, suspicious emails.

Users should be given security training, reinforced by strict network policies.

### 24. Threats to networks 2: malware

1 **Virus**: A virus is a computer program that is hidden within another program or file. It can replicate itself and infect other programs or files. Viruses are usually designed to have a harmful effect, for example corrupting or deleting data on a disk.

**Trojans**: Trojans do not replicate or attach themselves to other files. Trojans are installed by a computer user who thinks they are installing legitimate software or by opening an email attachment. Trojans can be annoying, for example by changing the desktop and adding new icons. Trojans can be malicious, for example by deleting files and destroying system information. They can also create 'back doors' to computer systems which allow criminals to access personal data.

**Spyware**: Spyware is software that is installed when it is packaged with legitimate software. Spyware spies on the computer and sends information such as login names, passwords and account details to a criminal.

**Worm**: A worm is a program that copies itself and then infects other computers, usually by sending emails to everyone in a user's email address book or contact list. Worms take up computer resources, so an infected computer will run slowly. Worms can also be used to take over computer systems remotely.

2 Any four from:
- Install antivirus software and ensure that it is constantly updated.
- Ensure that antivirus software can scan emails.
- Use adware removal software.
- Use anti-spyware software.
- Avoid opening emails and attachments or downloading software from unknown sources.
- Install a firewall to ensure that software is not downloaded without your knowledge.
- Ensure that the operating system is up to date.
- Install the latest security updates.

### 25. Threats to networks 3: network security

1 (a) **Brute force attacks** are general attacks which need little specialist knowledge or techniques. Automated software is used to try millions of different passwords.

(b) **SQL injection**: In SQL injection, criminals input specially created commands instead of a username or password. These commands gain access to the database so that the criminals have access to users' data.

**Denial of service** attacks flood a network or website with useless network communications, such as repeated login requests, which prevent legitimate users from gaining access to the network or website.

**Data interception and theft:** Criminals use packet analysers (packet sniffers) to intercept network packets. The packets are analysed and decoded. This allows criminals to steal sensitive data such as logins, passwords, credit card numbers and PINs.

2 Any two from:
- to extort money from the company to stop the attacks
- to reduce or eliminate competition on behalf of a rival company
- to punish a company that they deem to be unethical.

### 26. Identifying and preventing vulnerabilities 1

1 (a) (i) Any two from: smartphones, MP3 players, USB flash drives, portable hard disk drives, SD cards.

(ii) Any two from: Data can be stolen or removed without permission; malware can be introduced; software can be installed.

(b) Any three from:
- They should be a certain length and composed of alphanumeric and punctuation characters.
- They should never contain a user's identifiable information such as name, date of birth, phone number, postcode, car registration etc.
- They should be changed regularly.
- Users should not reuse previous passwords.
- They should never be written down.
- They should never be shared with other users.

(c) (i) Penetration testing is used to:
- find vulnerabilities in computer systems and networks that an attacker could exploit
- test the effectiveness of network security policies.

(ii) User access control gives folder and file rights to network users. It stipulates which files they are allowed to read, edit or delete. The users will therefore not be able to view restricted information or change and delete files that they are not allowed access to.

### 27. Identifying and preventing vulnerabilities 2

1 **Measure 1:** The organisation should install and configure a firewall to prevent people from gaining unauthorised access to its network via the internet, and also to control employees' access to the internet from the network.

**Measure 2:** Anti-malware software should be installed and used, to detect and remove malware. The anti-malware software should be constantly updated to tackle new threats.
**Measure 3:** Encryption should be used for sensitive communications into and out of the organisation, and for data storage.

2   New security features are continually being introduced to combat new malware and forms of attack.

# SYSTEM SOFTWARE
## 28. Operating systems 1

1   Systems software's role is to control the operation of the computer hardware, allow software to run, provide an interface for computer users, maintain the computer system and manage user interactions with the computer system.

2   (a) The operating system checks that memory requests are valid, allocates memory to processes when needed and frees up memory for other uses when no longer needed. It also swaps out data to the virtual memory when the main memory is full.
    (b) File management is used to create a folder and file structure for data. This makes it easier for users to organise and find data in a systematic way.
    (c) File permissions control who can create a file, who can see or open a file, who can write to a file or edit it and who can delete a file.

## 29. Operating systems 2

1   **Managing computer users**. The operating system:
    • requires a login name for each individual user of a computer
    • requires each user to provide a password for security
    • creates folders in which users can store their work.
    When a user installs software, the operating system allows them to install it just for themselves or for all users.
    **Providing an interface**. The user interface:
    • allows the user to communicate with the computer
    • translates user input by the keyboard or mouse into a form that the computer hardware and software can understand and execute.
    Many operating systems provide a **graphical user interface (GUI)** while others allow the user to type in commands. These are called command line interfaces.

2   Peripherals are controlled by the operating system using programs called **drivers**. The drivers carry out the necessary translations to allow the CPU and the devices to communicate correctly.

## 30. Utility system software

1   (a) Data is fragmented when parts of files are saved to different parts of the hard disk.
    (b) Defragmentation software reorganises files which have been split across different parts of the disk by putting pieces of related data back together. Fewer disk accesses are then needed to read the data. This improves performance and can free up more space on the hard disk.
    (c) (i)   When he is attaching a file to an email or uploading it to a website.
       (ii)  Lossless compression reduces the file size without discarding any of the data and the original file is restored when it is decompressed.
             Lossy compression reduces the file size by discarding some of the data, so the original file cannot be restored when it is decompressed.
    (d) (i)   Incremental backup.
       (ii)  Not all of the files are backed up each time – only the ones that have been added to or changed since the last backup.

2   Encryption software is used to scramble data into a form that cannot be used by unauthorised users. This protects the data from unauthorised use.

# ETHICAL, LEGAL, CULTURAL AND ENVIRONMENTAL CONCERNS
## 31. Ethical and legal issues

(a) The users of devices should consider the implications of continually upgrading or changing them because of the effects on the environment. The manufacture and disposal of the devices consumes large amounts of energy. Most of this energy is derived from non-renewable resources such as fossil fuels, which has an impact on the environment and contributes to global warming.
   The devices can be harmful if they are sent to landfill sites for disposal, because toxic waste substances (lead, mercury and cobalt) can get into the land and water.
   It can be argued that continually changing devices can be ethical because it provides employment for the people making them. Old equipment can be given to people around the world who are not able to afford their own.
   The legal responsibilities of users are to recycle their equipment using an official recycling firm. Devices may be dumped in developing countries. It is the ethical responsibility of users to check what happens to them and ensure that they are recycled by reputable companies.

(b) File sharing is unethical as it deprives the creators of the work of payment for their work. If a user obtains a copy of someone's work without paying for it, it is the same as stealing or shoplifting. Without payment, the professional artists will not be able to continue creating their works. It has been estimated that about 50% of jobs in the film industry have been lost by the copying and sharing of videos. Peer-to-peer sharing therefore creates unemployment.
   File sharing is illegal as it contravenes the Copyright Designs and Patents Act 1988. Sanctions for breaking the Copyright Designs and Patents Act 1988 include being fined or being prevented from using the internet.

(c) Using another person's password to gain unauthorised access to a computer or a network is illegal under the Computer Misuse Act 1990.
   It is also unethical. The student is trying to gain an unfair advantage over fellow students by looking at the past papers and model answers. They are not behaving in a way which individuals and society regards reflecting good values.

## 32. Cultural issues 1

1   (a) Teachers at the school.
    (b) **Teachers will:**
        • require training to learn how to use the new system
        • need computers, smartphones or tablets in order to run the new system
        • be able to quickly produce attendance reports and see attendance patterns among the students
        • be able send data electronically to the parents.
    (c) (i)   Any two from:
              • They may not be able to afford equipment.
              • They may have low IT literacy.
              • There may not be the infrastructure available to them, e.g. no broadband.
       (ii)  Any two from:
              • They will not be able to communicate electronically, e.g. by using emails and video conferencing, and may miss important messages and information.
              • They will not be able to pay bills online and therefore may have to pay more.
              • They will not be able to shop online, so will have less choice and may have to pay more for items.
              • Anyone who is unemployed will not be able to search for jobs online and may have their benefits suspended.
              • They will not be qualified for some jobs as they will not be able to work remotely from home.
        Similar answers are also acceptable.

### 33. Cultural issues 2

1 Your answer could include some of the following ideas.
Computer science technology has had a huge impact on the ways in which people communicate.

In areas of the world without telecommunications infrastructure and where there are no land lines, mobile phones have allowed people to communicate using voice calls for the first time.

All people can now communicate instantly using emails, text and multimedia messages and video conferencing. Files including spreadsheets, word processed documents and images can be attached to emails and sent instantly. People can also communicate with many people at once using social and personal networking sites and blogs. Computer science technology has allowed for more and instantaneous communication between people. This can sometimes be a disadvantage as they may communicate things that they later wished they had not.

Accessing the internet from computers, tablets and smartphones has allowed people to communicate news items. This has been especially useful in countries with repressive governments who do not let official news agencies report on what is going on.

It can be argued that the technology has led to the creation of more communities through improved communications. Social networking sites are communities where people can communicate through text, sound and video messages.

### 34. Environmental issues

1 Your answer could include some of the following ideas.
**Energy**

Manufacture and use of devices uses energy. Manufacturing involves energy-intensive mining and processing of minerals. The use of devices involves the energy used by the devices themselves, but also by data centres. These data centres generate heat, so energy is needed to keep them cool. Much of the energy used comes from non-renewable sources such as gas and coal.

Computer science is used in efficient energy production. Computer software is used to design, model and test efficient devices to produce electricity from wind, wave and solar power.

Energy use can be reduced using smart technologies, such as light-sensitive switches that turn off lights when they are not needed.

Efficient transport planning using computer modelling and analysis can reduce fuel use.

**Sustainability**

Digital devices use many different chemical elements. Some of these are rare and will be in short supply as they are used up. It is difficult to recycle devices to reuse these elements.

**Waste**

Electronic devices are difficult to recycle and are often disposed of in landfill sites as e-waste. Landfill sites take up areas of land that could be used for other purposes. Toxic substances such as lead, mercury and cobalt can get into the soil and the water supply from the landfill sites and cause health problems.

**Data analysis**

Computer science technology can be used to monitor environmental factors by transmitting and analysing data. This data can be shared by scientists around the world who can collaborate to find solutions to problems. Computers can be used to develop models to forecast environmental behaviour and identify options for action.

### 35. Privacy issues

1 Computer science technology allows companies and government organisations to find out details of people's activities and to track their movements.

Surveillance cameras are commonplace in most towns and cities in Britain. With the advent of number plate recognition, it has been claimed that a person can be tracked on a journey through London in a car and on foot. Britain has more surveillance cameras per head of population than any other country in Europe.

Many people have complained that being tracked, filmed and photographed without their permission is an infringement of their privacy.

Mobile phone use allows people's movements to be tracked as they move to different cells or mobile phone masts. This can be considered as an infringement of one's privacy.

Internet service providers and companies such as Google record every search carried out and website visited. This can be used to find out what users are interested in and target advertisements directly at them. This can be considered as an infringement of privacy, especially if the companies hand over this information to the government authorities.

Surveillance cameras help prevent antisocial behaviour. If criminals know they are being filmed, they will not attack people and property. Criminal acts can also be stopped if they are seen on surveillance cameras. Videos from surveillance cameras can be used as evidence in criminal prosecutions.

Surveillance cameras can help to find missing people. Some people say that people shouldn't be worried if they are not doing anything wrong but others argue that it is dangerous for governments to be able to know exactly what you are doing and where you are.

Tracking a person using their mobile phone can help to solve crimes and verify that criminals were in a particular area. The analysis of huge amounts of personal data can lead to better-informed decision making and planning such as improvements in public health and smarter cities geared to the movements of their inhabitants.

### 36. Legislation 1

1 (a) Data Protection Act 1988
   (b) Any three from:
   - Inspect and check the data held, but the organisations can charge us for this
   - Demand that incorrect information is amended
   - Demand that the data is not used in any way that could harm or distress us
   - Demand that any data held by the organisation is not used for direct marketing.
   (c) Any three from:
   - To keep it secure
   - Not to ask for more data than is necessary
   - Not to keep data any longer than necessary
   - To keep data accurate and up to date
   - Not to use the data for any other purpose without our consent.

**2**

| Action | Type of offence |
|---|---|
| A student accesses another student's email account without permission. | A |
| A user accesses parents' stored credit card numbers and security codes in order to buy goods online fraudulently. | C |
| A student guesses the login names and passwords of other students and logs into their accounts. | A |
| A student gains access to class results and changes their own marks and grades. | B |
| As a challenge, a student manages to guess the password of one of the administrative staff to gain entry to the management system. | A |

## 37. Legislation 2

1 (a) All original work, including images, music, documents and videos.
 (b) The person who creates the work owns the copyright.
 (c) For example:
   1 The person could be sent to prison.
   2 The person could be prevented from using the internet by their internet service provider.
2 (a) For example:
   1 So that others can include their work and include it within their own with or without attribution depending on the type of licence.
   2 So that others can modify and build upon their work and re-distributed.
 (b) **Public domain:** There are no restrictions. It can be used without permission or attribution for any purpose.
   **Attribution-non-commercial:** The work can be used, distributed and copied as long as the creator is given credit for having created it and it is used for non-commercial purposes.
3 Freedom of Information Act 2000

## 38. Proprietary and open-source software

1 (a) Proprietary software is commercially produced by an organisation for a profit.
 (b) Any one from:
   • Software is developed professionally and carefully tested.
   • Support will be provided to keep customers happy so that they will continue to use the software.
   • There will be books, magazine articles and online tutorials.
   • Updates and bug fixes meet the needs and suggestions of the users.

(c) Any one from:
   • Users can study the source code to see how the software works.
   • Users can change and upgrade the software.
   • It is free to use.
   • There is a community of dedicated enthusiasts who will provide help and support.

**2**

| Statement | Proprietary | Open-source |
|---|---|---|
| The source code cannot be modified by anyone but the person, team, or organisation that created it. | ✓ | |
| It is free to use. | | ✓ |
| Users can modify the source code to adapt it to their needs and can pass it on to other users free of charge. | | ✓ |
| The software must be paid for. | ✓ | |
| Users can study the source code to see how the software works. | | ✓ |
| It may need specialist knowledge to install the software. | | ✓ |
| The support and updates may be expensive. | ✓ | |
| The software will be developed carefully and tested thoroughly because people will be paying money to use it and they will be cross if it doesn't work. | ✓ | |
| There is a community of dedicated enthusiasts who will provide help and support. | | ✓ |

# ALGORITHMS

## 39. Computational thinking

1 (a) Abstraction means removing unnecessary detail to focus on the important elements.
 (b) 'computerTurn' is an abstraction because it is a model or simulation of a real-life activity. The programmer doesn't need to know how the sub-program works – only that it returns an appropriate value.
 (c) One possible algorithm is shown below. You could also use a switch/case construct (see page 55 of the Revision Guide). All solutions should compare the computer and player choices and decide who is the winner.

```
function gameWinner(computerChoice, playerChoice)        //The choices of the computer and player are
                                                         passed to the function
//A check is first made to see if the game is a draw.
   If playerChoice == computerChoice then
      result = "Draw"
//Now all the possible combinations are checked
   elseif playerChoice == "R" AND computerChoice == "S" then
      result = "Player wins"
   elseif playerChoice == "R" AND computerChoice == "P" then
      result = "Player loses"
   elseif playerChoice == "S" AND computerChoice == "R" then
      result = "Player loses"
   elseif playerChoice == "S" AND computerChoice == "P" then
      result = "Player wins"
   elseif playerChoice == "P" AND computerChoice == "R" then
      result = "Player wins"
   elseif playerChoice == "P" AND computerChoice == "S" then
      result = "Player loses"
   endif
   return result                                         //The result is returned to the main program
endfunction
```

## 40. Algorithms

1  (a) An algorithm is a step-by-step procedure for solving problems.
   (b) 1   selection
       2   iteration
       3   selection
       4   sequence
       5   selection
       6   sequence
       7   iteration
       8   selection
       9   iteration
       10  selection
   (c) 1  Pseudocode.
       2  Flow diagrams.

## 41. Algorithms – pseudocode

1  (a) Pseudocode is similar to a high-level programming language, but does not require exact syntax/indentation to be used. The programmer can concentrate on getting the logic of the program correct before turning it into executable code.

   (b)
```
binaryNumber = input ("Please enter an 8-bit binary number.")
placeValues = [128, 64, 32, 16, 8, 4, 2, 1]        //An array stores the place values of the digits
denaryNumber = 0
//The digits will now be multiplied by their place values
for index = 0 to binaryNumber.length - 1
    denaryNumber = denaryNumber + (binaryNumber(index) * placeValues[index]
next index
print(denaryNumber)
```

## 42. Algorithms – flow diagrams

1  (a)

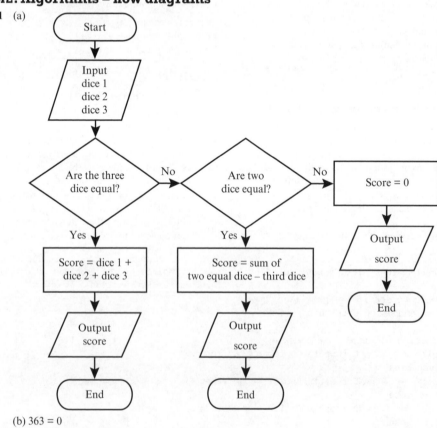

   (b) 363 = 0
       545 = 6
   (c) Any suitable e.g. 113, 114, 115, 116; 225, 226

## 43. Standard searching algorithms – linear search

**1** (a) A linear search algorithm starts at the beginning of a
list and moves through it item by item until it finds the
matching item or reaches the end of the list.

(b)

```
found = False
index = 0
while found == False AND index <= partyList.length - 1    //The loop will run until the name is found
                                                           or the end of the list is reached.
   if partyList[index] == "Elaine" then
      found = True
   endif
   index = index + 1
endwhile
if found == True then
   print("Elaine is on the list.")
else
   print("Elaine is not on the list")
endif
```

## 44. Standard searching algorithms – binary search

**1** Select the middle item (the median).
Compare this value with your search criterion. If they are
equal, then stop.
If your search criterion is lower, then repeat with the left-
hand side of the list.
If it is higher, repeat with the right-hand side of the list.
Repeat these steps until the search criterion is found or
there are no more items in the list to search.

**2** Ahmed Ann Claire David Mary Matt Peter Stephen Zoe
Select the median item – Mary.
Compare 'Stephen' with 'Mary'
New sub-list is 'Matt', 'Peter', 'Stephen', 'Zoe'
Compare 'Stephen' with 'Peter'.
New sub-list is 'Stephen', 'Zoe'.
Compare 'Stephen' with 'Stephen' – search item found

**3** Compare 9 with 28
New sub-list is 1, 6, 9, 13, 15, 21
Compare 9 with 9 – search item found

## 45. Comparing linear and binary searches

**1**

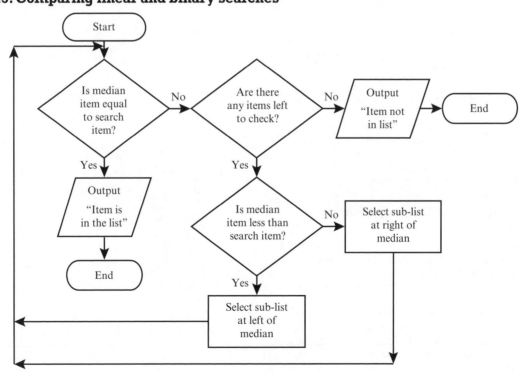

# Answers

**2** (a)

1..........**50**..........100    The first median is 50
1..........**25**..........49    The second median is 25
1..........**12**..........24    The third median is 12
1..........**6**..........11    The fourth median is 6
1..........**3**..........5    The fifth median is 3
1..........**1**..........2    The sixth median is 1
1

There is only one number left to select (2) and therefore the maximum number of selections is 7.

(b) For a binary search, the data must first be sorted into ascending order. Sorting the data will take time so, for a small number of search items, a linear search might find the search item more quickly.

A linear search would be more efficient than a binary search if the item being searched for is the first item in the list.

## 46. Standard sorting algorithms – bubble sort

**1**

|  | 20 | 15 | 3 | 13 | 9 | 2 | 6 |
|---|---|---|---|---|---|---|---|
| Pass 1 | 15 | 3 | 13 | 9 | 2 | 6 | 20 |
| Pass 2 | 3 | 13 | 9 | 2 | 6 | 15 | 20 |
| Pass 3 | 3 | 9 | 2 | 6 | 13 | 15 | 20 |
| Pass 4 | 3 | 2 | 6 | 9 | 13 | 15 | 20 |
| Pass 5 | 2 | 3 | 6 | 9 | 13 | 15 | 20 |

**2**

| Order | Line |
|---|---|
| 1 | swapped = True |
| 11 | next index |
| 4 | for index = 1 to list.length - 1 |
| 3 | swapped = False |
| 5 | if list[index – 1] > list[index] then |
| 9 | swapped = True |
| 10 | endif |
| 6 | temp = list[index – 1] |
| 2 | while swapped = True |
| 7 | list[index – 1] = list[index] |
| 12 | endwhile |
| 8 | list[index] = temp |

The marks will be awarded for the following:
1 mark for getting the start and end of the while loop in the correct positions
1 mark for getting the lines of the swap in the correct order
1 mark for getting the start and end of the 'if' statement in the correct positions
1 mark for setting the value of swapped correctly
5 marks for getting all lines correct.

## 47. Standard sorting algorithms – insertion sort

**1** Start with the second item and compare it with the first. If it's larger than the first, then leave it in place, but if it's smaller, swap the two numbers.
Now check the third number. If it's smaller than the second one, then compare it with the first.
If it is smaller than the first, place it in this position by moving the first two numbers along.
Repeat this procedure with all the numbers by comparing them with the numbers to the left until a smaller number is found. When it is, place the number in the position to the right of it by moving the others along.

**2**

| 6 | 3 | 12 | 9 | 7 | 11 | 1 |
|---|---|---|---|---|---|---|
| 3 | 6 | 12 | 9 | 7 | 11 | 1 |
| 3 | 6 | 9 | 12 | 7 | 11 | 1 |
| 3 | 6 | 7 | 9 | 12 | 11 | 1 |
| 3 | 6 | 7 | 9 | 11 | 12 | 1 |
| 1 | 3 | 6 | 7 | 9 | 11 | 12 |

**3**

| Ravish | Sean | Elsie | Alice | Rosie | Jack | Ollie |
|---|---|---|---|---|---|---|
| Ravish | Sean | Elsie | Alice | Rosie | Jack | Ollie |
| Elsie | Ravish | Sean | Alice | Rosie | Jack | Ollie |
| Alice | Elsie | Ravish | Sean | Rosie | Jack | Ollie |
| Alice | Elsie | Ravish | Rosie | Sean | Jack | Ollie |
| Alice | Elsie | Jack | Ravish | Rosie | Sean | Ollie |
| Alice | Elsie | Jack | Ollie | Ravish | Rosie | Sean |

## 48. Standard sorting algorithms – merge sort

**1** (a) Each small sub-problem is easier to solve than one large problem.
It is more efficient to combine the solutions than to try to solve the main problem without using any techniques.

(b) Recursion involves repeating a process using the results of the first application.

**2**

| 33 | 25 | 46 | 2 | 8 | 69 | 9 |
|---|---|---|---|---|---|---|

33 25 46 2 | 8 69 9
33 25 | 46 2 | 8 69 | 9
33 | 25 | 46 | 2 | 8 | 69 | 9
25 33 | 2 46 | 8 69 | 9
2 25 38 46 | 8 9 69

| 2 | 8 | 9 | 25 | 33 | 46 | 69 |
|---|---|---|---|---|---|---|

### 49. Interpreting, correcting and completing algorithms

1

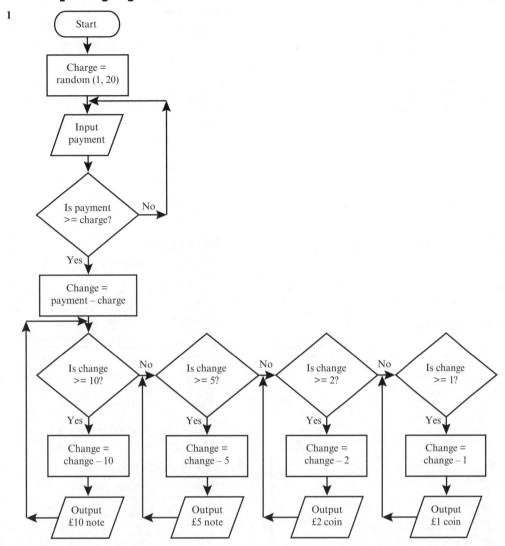

### 50. Using trace tables

1 (a) An array.

(b) (i) line 4

(ii) for search = 0 to list.length – 1

(c)

| item | found | search | list[search] | output |
|------|-------|--------|--------------|--------|
| 13 | False | 0 | 5 | |
| 13 | False | 1 | 9 | |
| 13 | False | 2 | 2 | |
| 13 | False | 3 | 5 | |
| 13 | True | 4 | 13 | |
| 13 | True | 4 | 13 | "The item is in the list." |

## PROGRAMMING TECHNIQUES

### 51. Variables and constants

1 (a) A variable is a container which is used to store values which can change as the program is running.

(b) The value stored in a variable can change during program execution, whereas the content of a constant always stays the same.

(c) They should be given meaningful names so that anyone reading the code will be given an indication of the types of value they are intended to contain e.g. 'studentAge' rather than just 'X'.

(d)

| Variable | Use within the program |
|----------|------------------------|
| mysteryNumber | This is used to hold the number which must be guessed. |
| correct | This is a 'flag' used to indicate whether the search item is in the list when it changes to True. |
| guess | This is used so that the user can enter a number. |

### 52. Arithmetic operators

1 (a) result = 6 * 8 / 2 + (15 – 6) + 3^3 (Brackets)

result = 6 * 8 / 2 + 9 + 3^3 (Indexes)

result = 6 * 4 + 9 + 9 (Division)

result = 6 * 8 / 2 + 9 + 9 (Multiplication)

result = 24 + 9 + 9 (Addition)

result = 42

2

| Code | Resultnumber |
|------|--------------|
| number = 12 + 6 / 2 | 15 |
| number = 6 * 3 / 2 | 9 |
| number = 23 MOD 6 | 5 |
| number = 23 DIV 6 | 3 |
| number = 6 ^ 2 | 36 |

3
```
number = input("Please enter a number.")
result = number * 2
result = result + 6
result = result / 2
result = result - number
print(result)
```

## 53. Comparison operators

**1**

| Statement | True/False |
|---|---|
| 7 * 3 != 10 + 11 | False |
| 8 + 10 > 8 * 2 | True |
| 9 * 3 <= 10 + 17 | True |
| 10 + 15 >= 6 * 5 | False |
| 9 * 2 == 6 * 3 | True |

**2**
```
newMark = input("Please enter the new mark.")
equal = 0
less = 0
greater = 0
for index = 0 to marks.length - 1
    if marks[index] == newMark then
        equal = equal +1
    elseif marks[index] < newMark then
        less = less + 1
    else
        greater = greater + 1
    endif
next index
print("Equal = " + equal + "Less = " + less +
"Greater = " + greater)
```

## 54. Boolean operators

| Algorithm | Output |
|---|---|
| `number = 3`<br>`if number > 0 AND number < 2 then`<br>    `print("Within range.")`<br>`else`<br>    `print("Out of range.")`<br>`endif` | Out of range. |
| `number = 6`<br>`if NOT(number = 3) OR number != 5 then`<br>    `print("Number is acceptable.")`<br>`else`<br>    `print("Number is not acceptable.")`<br>`endif` | Number is acceptable. |
| `colour = "red"`<br>`size = "m"`<br>`price = 25`<br>`if colour = "blue" OR colour = "red"`<br>`AND size == "m" AND price <= 30 then`<br>    `print("This would be OK.")`<br>`else`<br>    `print("Not OK.")`<br>`endif` | This would be OK. |
| `number1 = 6`<br>`number2 = 9`<br>`if (number1 <= 9 OR number2 >=10)`<br>`AND NOT(number1 * number2 <50) AND`<br>`number2 - number1 == 3 then`<br>    `print("These numbers are OK.")`<br>`else`<br>    `print("Not OK.")`<br>`endif` | These numbers are OK. |

## 55. Selection
```
result = input("Please enter a mark between 0 and
100")
if result >= 90 then
    print("Excellent")
elseif result >= 70 then
    print("Very good")
elseif result >= 60 then
    print("Good")
elseif result >= 50 then
    print("Satisfactory")
else
```

```
    print("Unsatisfactory")
endif
```

## 56. Iteration
```
list = [5, 9, 2, 5, 13]
item = input("Please enter the search item.")
found = False
search = 0
while found == False AND search <= item.length - 1
    if item == list[search] then
        found = true
    endif
    search = search + 1
endwhile
if found == True then
    print("The item is in the list")
else
    print("The item is not in the list.")
endif
```

## 57. Data types

**1** (a)

| Data type | Variable |
|---|---|
| String | name |
| Real | meanHoursWorked |
| Boolean | fullWeek |
| Integer | day, oneDay, hoursWorked, daysWorked |
| Character | gender |

(b) Variables will be needed for the pay per hour and the
pay for the week.
Variable 1: payPerHour
Data type: Real
Variable 2: payForWeek
Data type: Real

## 58. String manipulation

**1**

| Variable | Value |
|---|---|
| Subject.length | 16 |
| position | 8 |
| partSubject | put |

**2**
```
sentence = input("Please enter a sentence.").lower
        //The sentence is converted to lower case.
a = 0
e = 0
i = 0
o = 0
u = 0
for index = 0 to sentence.length - 1
    if sentence(index) == "a" then
        a = a + 1
    elseif sentence(index) == "e" then
        e = e + 1
    elseif sentence(index) == "i" then
        i = i + 1
    elseif sentence(index) == "o" then
        o = o + 1
    elseif sentence(index) == "u" then
        u = u + 1
    endif
next index
print("a = " + a + " e = " + e + " i = " + i + " o
= " + o + " u = " + u + ".")
```

## 59. Arrays

**1** (a) An array is a data structure that can store multiple items
of data, called elements, which are all of the same data
type under the same identifier.

(b) (i)  array temp[7]

   (ii)  One possible solution is shown below. An alternative
      solution would be to set both max and min initially
      to the first element of the array and then loop
      through the remaining elements.

```
max = 0
min = 45
for index = 0 to temp.length - 1
    if temp[index] > max then
        max = temp[index]
    endif
    if temp[index] < min then
        min = temp[index]
    endif
next index
print("Maximum = " + max + " and minimum = " + min)
```

2

|   | 0 | 1 | 2 | 3 |
|---|---|---|---|---|
| **0** | 0 | 1 | 1 | 0 |
| **1** | 1 | 0 | 0 | 1 |
| **2** | 1 | 1 | 1 | 1 |
| **3** | 1 | 0 | 0 | 1 |

## 60. File handling operations

1  (a)

```
myFile = openWrite("shape.txt")
    for index = 0 to pixels.length - 1
        myFile.writeLine(pixels(index))
    next index
myFile(close)
```

(b)

```
myFile = openRead("shape.txt")              //The text file is opened in read mode
    while NOT myFile.endOfFile()            //The loop will run until the end of the file is
                                            reached

        for row = 0 to 3                    //A loop is set up for the 4 rows of the matrix
            for index = 0 to 3              //A nested loop is set up for the 4 items in each row
            matrix[row, index] = myFile.readLine()   //The saved data is read into each item
        next index
    next row
    endwhile
myFile(close)
```

## 61. Records

1  (a) (i)  The field **Name** is shown. Other fields are **Gender**, **Weight**, **Number of days**, **Special diet?**

   (ii)  The record for Jack is shown. The equivalent row for Dottie is also a record.

(b) Name – string

   Gender – character

   Weight – real

   Number of days – integer

   Special diet? – character

(c) The entry should be a length of 1 and be either 'F' OR 'M'.

(d) (i)  A key field must contain unique data in each record. The same data could appear more than once in any of the fields in this table.

   (ii)  She could give each cat a unique registration number.

## 62. Structured query language

1 (a) 4
(b) WHERE TimesPlayed >= 15;
(c) (i) SELECT Title, Length, Medium
FROM COLLECTION
WHERE Artist LIKE "Charlie Charles";
(ii) SELECT Title, TimesPlayed, Medium
FROM COLLECTION
WHERE Artist LIKE "Charlie Charles" OR Artist
LIKE "Bob Guthrie";

## 63. Sub-programs 1

1 (a) A sub-program is a self-contained sequence of program
instructions that performs a specific task and is called
whenever it is needed to carry out that task.
(b) 1 They make programs shorter. The code only needs to be
written once and can be called as many times as needed.
2 They make testing easier as each section of code only
has to be tested once even though it is used many
times.
(c) A function returns data to the main program but a
procedure does not.
2 (a) measurement
(b) newMeasurement
(c) return newMeasurement

## 64. Sub-programs 2

1 (a) Any two from: recLength, recWidth, recArea,
recCircumference
(b) For example: length, width
(c) For example: area, circumference
(d) recArea, recCircumference = calculate(recLength, recWidth)
2
```
function findLargest(one, two)
    if one > two then
        largest = one
    else
        largest = two
    return largest
endfunction
//Main program
numberOne = input("Please enter the first number")
numberTwo = input("Please enter the second number.")
largestNumber = findlargest(numberOne, numberTwo)
print(largestNumber)
```

## PRODUCING ROBUST PROGRAMS

## 65. Defensive design

```
1.  validated == False
2.  while validated == False
3.      validated = True
4.      password = input("Please enter a password.")
5.      while password == ""
6.          print("You have not made an entry.")
7.          password = input("Please enter a password.")
8.      endwhile
9.      if password.length < 8 then
10.         print("Password is less than 8 characters in length.")
11.         validated = False
12.     endif
13.     numberUpper = 0
14.     for index = 0 to password.length – 1
15.         if ASC(password(index)) >= 65 AND ASC(password(index)) <= 90 then
16.             numberUpper = numberUpper + 1
17.         endif
18.     next index
19.     if numberUpper == 0 then
20.         print("No upper case letters.")
21.         validated = False
22.     endif
23. endwhile
24. print("Password OK.")
```

## 66. Testing and maintainabilty

1 (a)

| Test number | Type of test | Test data | Expected result |
|---|---|---|---|
| 1 | Normal data test | 69 | Data will be accepted |
| 2 | Boundary data test | 99 | Data will be accepted |
| 3 | Erroneous data test | 120 | Data will not be accepted and an error message will be shown |

(b)

| Line number | Correct version |
|---|---|
| 2 | for index = 0 to students.length - 1 |
| 7 | marks[index] = percentage |
| 8 | if percentage > maximum then |

## COMPUTATIONAL LOGIC

## 67. Computational logic 1

1 AND, NOT, OR

2

| A | B | C | D | Q |
|---|---|---|---|---|
| 0 | 0 | 0 | 0 | 0 |
| 0 | 0 | 1 | 0 | 1 |
| 0 | 1 | 0 | 0 | 0 |
| 0 | 1 | 1 | 0 | 1 |
| 1 | 0 | 0 | 0 | 0 |
| 1 | 0 | 1 | 0 | 1 |
| 1 | 1 | 0 | 1 | 1 |
| 1 | 1 | 1 | 1 | 1 |

3 (A OR B) AND C

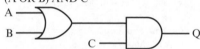

## 68. Computational logic 2

1

| A | B | P |
|---|---|---|
| 0 | 0 | 0 |
| 0 | 1 | 1 |
| 1 | 0 | 0 |
| 1 | 1 | 0 |

2 (a)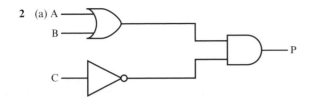

| A | B | C | P |
|---|---|---|---|
| 0 | 0 | 0 | 0 |
| 0 | 0 | 1 | 0 |
| 0 | 1 | 0 | 1 |
| 0 | 1 | 1 | 0 |
| 1 | 0 | 0 | 1 |
| 1 | 0 | 1 | 0 |
| 1 | 1 | 0 | 1 |
| 1 | 1 | 1 | 0 |

## TRANSLATORS AND FACILITIES OF LANGUAGES

### 69. Programming languages

1 (a) Assembly language.
  (b) Machine language or machine code.
  (c) Language 1 is a high-level language as it is very similar to a human language. It has to be translated before it can be processed by the CPU. Language 2 is a low-level language as it is very similar to machine code and each command represents a similar command in language 3. Language 3 is a low-level language because it can be directly processed by the CPU.
  You could also answer by saying that languages 2 and 3 are at a low level of abstraction while language 1 is at a high level of abstraction.
  (d) (i)  1 It is less time consuming to write and then test the program as the language is similar to a human language.
    2 High-level programs are portable from one machine to another as they are independent of the CPU.
    (ii)  1 Programs written in low-level languages require less memory and execution time.
    2 They allow the programmer to directly control system hardware and are used extensively for programming embedded systems.

### 70. Translators

1 (a) An assembler.
  (b) A compiler translates the source code into a standalone, machine code program (object code) which can then be executed by the processor. An interpreter translates the high-level code line by line. It is needed each time the program is run.
  (c) An advantage of a compiler is that the program is translated once only and as a separate process. When it is run, it is already translated into machine code so it is executed more rapidly. A disadvantage is that you cannot change the program without going back to the original source code, editing that and recompiling.
  An advantage of an interpreter is that when an error is found, the interpreter reports it and stops so the programmer knows where the error has occurred. A disadvantage is that every line has to be translated every time it is executed and therefore it is slower.
2 The set-top box must process data quickly and so a compiler is used because compiled code runs faster than interpreted code.

### 71. Integrated development environment

1 (a) A syntax error is when a grammatical rule of the program language is broken.
  It could be a misspelling, e.g. prnit instead of print, or it could be missing brackets or speech marks.

(b) Three facilities are shown here. Your answer should include two of these.
  • Autocomplete or word completion. This involves the source code editor predicting a word or phrase that the user wants to type in without the user actually typing it in completely. For example, if the user types a 'p', the editor might suggest the word 'print'. Therefore the user will not have to enter it themselves and misspell it.
  • Bracket matching highlights matching sets of delimiters such as brackets or quotation marks. It helps the programmer navigate through the code and spot any that do not match, which would cause syntax errors.
  • Auto-indentation. This feature will automatically indent the next line to the correct level when the return key is pressed. In some languages, indentation is a requirement.
(c) (i)  Variable tracing. This feature allows the programmer to see the values of variables at any stage in the running of the program.
  (ii)  Breakpoints. Breakpoints are the intentional stopping of the program at specified places so that the programmer can inspect the code and see if the program is functioning as expected up to that point.

## DATA REPRESENTATION

### 72. Data representation

1 (a) binary
  (b) Processing is carried out by billions of transistors which operate in one of two states, on and off, equivalent to 1 and 0.

2

| byte | mega-byte | tera-byte | bit | peta-byte | kilo-byte | giga-byte | nibble |
|------|-----------|-----------|-----|-----------|-----------|-----------|--------|
| 3 | 5 | 7 | 1 | 8 | 4 | 6 | 2 |

3 72 000 000 000 bits = 72 000 000 000/8 bytes = 9 000 000 000 bytes
9 000 000 000 bytes = 9 000 000 000/1000 kilobytes = 9 000 000 kilobytes
9 000 000 kilobytes = 9 000 000/1000 megabytes = 9 000 megabytes
9 000 megabytes = 9000/1000 gigabytes = 9 gigabytes
4 20 megabytes = 20 × 1000 kilobytes = 20 000 kilobytes = 20 000 000 bytes = 160 000 000 bits

### 73. Converting from denary to binary

1

| Comparison | Binary digit | Remainder |
|------------|--------------|-----------|
| 199 > 128 | 1 | 71 |
| 71 > 64 | 1 | 7 |
| 7 < 32 | 0 | 7 |
| 7 < 16 | 0 | 7 |
| 7 < 8 | 0 | 7 |
| 7 > 4 | 1 | 3 |
| 3 > 2 | 1 | 1 |
| 1 = 1 | 1 | 0 |

11000111
2 There are a number of different algorithms that could be used. The one given here stores the place values in an array and the place values are then used in a loop. You could also use a longer algorithm without the array where the place values are individually used one after the other in the code.

```
decimal = input("Please enter the decimal number.")
binary = ""
placeValues = [128, 64, 32, 16, 8, 4, 2, 1]
for index = 0 to placeValues.length - 1
   if placeValues[index] >= decimal then
      binary = binary + "1"
      decimal = decimal - placeValues[index]
   else
      binary = binary + "0"
   endif
next index
print(binary)
```

### 74. Converting from binary to denary and binary addition

**1**

| Binary | 1 | 0 | 0 | 1 | 0 | 1 | 1 | 1 |
|---|---|---|---|---|---|---|---|---|
| Place values | 128 | 64 | 32 | 16 | 8 | 4 | 2 | 1 |
| Decimal | 128 | 0 | 0 | 16 | 0 | 4 | 2 | 1 |

The answer can be calculated using a table like the one shown here. However, you don't need to use a table, but you must show the additions of the separate place values:

Decimal = 128 + 16 + 4 + 2 + 1 = 151

**2** 
```
  0 1 0 1 0 1 1 1
  0 1 0 1 1 1 1 1
 ₁1 0 ₁1 ₁1 ₁0 ₁1 ₁1 0
```

**3** (a)
```
  1 1 0 0 1 0 1 1
    1 0 0 1 0 1 1 1
  1 0 1 ₁1 ₁0 ₁0 ₁0 ₁1 0
```

(b) (i) Overflow error.

(ii) The result produces a number that is greater than can be represented by 8 bits, so 9 bits are required. In denary, the number is greater than 255.

**4** Incorrect
```
  0 1 0 1 0 1 1 1
  0 1 0 0 1 0 1 0
 ₁1 0 ₁1 ₁0 ₁0 ₁0 0 1
```

### 75. Binary shifts

**1** (a) A binary shift is used when a binary number is being multiplied or divided by powers of 2. Shifts to the left are used for multiplication. Shifts to the right are used for division. A 1 place shift multiplies or divides by $2^1$ (2). A 2 place shift multiplies or divides by $2^2$ (4).

(b) 10101100

**2** (a) The binary number would be divided by 4.

(b)

| Binary number (dividend) | 10101101 | Denary equivalent | 173 |
|---|---|---|---|
| Binary number after a 2 place right shift (quotient) | 00101011 | Denary equivalent | 43 |

(c) In a 2 place right shift, the binary number is being divided by 4. The expected answer would be 43.2 but there is a loss of precision as the result in binary is given to the nearest lower integer (whole number) because the answer does not have decimal places.

### 76. Hexadecimal and denary

**1** (a) 9C = 9 * 16 + 12 = 144 + 12 = 156

(b) 249/16 = 15 with a remainder of 9

15/16 = 0 with a remainder of 15

Hexadecimal number = F9

**2**

```
function hexToDecimal(hex              //The function is defined with the variable 'hexadecimal' as a
                                       parameter
    decimal = 0
    for index = 0 to 1                 //A loop is set up to examine the two digits of the
                                       hexadecimal number
    number = hex(index)                //The variable 'number' is assigned a digit of the
                                       hexadecimal number
    if hex(index) == "A" then
       number = 10                     //The letters used in hexadecimal must be converted to their
                                       decimal equivalents
       elseif hex(index) == "B" then
          number = 11
       elseif hex(index) == "C" then
          number = 12
       elseif hex(index) == "D" then
          number = 13
       elseif hex(index) == "E" then
          number = 14
       elseif hex(index) == "F" then
          number = 15
    endif
    if index == 0 then
       decimal = decimal + number * 16)  //The first number must be multiplied by 16.
    else
       decimal = decimal + number
    endif
  next index
  return decimal
endfunction
```

## 77. Hexadecimal and binary

1   (a) Hexadecimal is used because people get confused with large binary numbers. Binary numbers can be simplified by writing them in hexadecimal notation, which means that fewer numbers are needed.

   (b) C3 is equal to the decimal numbers 12 and 3.
   12 and 3 represent the two nibbles of the binary number. Therefore the binary number = 1100 and 0011 = 11000011.

   (c) 11010101 = the two nibbles 1101 and 0101.
   These are equal to the two decimal numbers 13 and 5. Therefore the hexadecimal number = D5.
   10111101 = 1011 and 1101 = 11 and 13 = BD.

## 78. Check digits

1   (a) The purpose of a check digit is to verify that data such as a sequence of numbers has been entered correctly.

   (b)

| Number | 6 | 3 | 8 | 9 |
|---|---|---|---|---|
| Weighting | 5 | 4 | 3 | 2 |
| Multiplication | 30 | 12 | 24 | 18 |

   Total = 84
   Division by 11 = 7 remainder 7
   Subtract remainder from 11 = 4
   Check digit = 4

   (c) One possible answer is shown below. There are other possible solutions.

```
number = ("Please enter the 5 digit number.")
total = 0
index = 0
weighting = 5                       //The number at index position 0 must be multiplied by 5, the one at 2
                                    by 4 etc. As the index increases the weighting has to decrease
while index <= 4
   total = total + weighting * int(number(index))     //The number at the index position of the string
                                                       must be cast as a number for the multiplication
   weighting = weighting - 1
   index = index + 1
endwhile
remainder = total MOD 11          //The arithmetic operator MOD is used to find the remainder
if remainder = 0 then
   print("This number is valid.")
else
   print("This number is not valid.")
endif
```

## 79. Characters

1   (a) The character set is the list of binary codes that can be recognised by the computer hardware and software.

   (b) ASCII is a 7-bit code. There are 128 code sequences representing English characters and control actions such as SPACE and SHIFT. The codes are grouped according to function, e.g. codes 65 to 90 represent the upper case letters of the alphabet.

   (c) Unicode uses up to 32 bits to represent over 1 million characters. The ASCII code uses 7 bits to store 128 characters.

2
```
function convert(text)
   code = ""
   for index = 0 to text.length - 1
      code = code + ASC(text(index))
   next index
   return code
endfunction
//This is the main program
textEntry = input("Please enter the text")
codeString = convert(textEntry)
print(codeString)
```

## 80. Images

1   (a) The size of an image is given as the number of pixels in its width (W) and height (H).
   The resolution of an image is the number of pixels per unit area of the display.

   (b)

| Colour depth | Number of colours represented |
|---|---|
| 1 | 2 |
| 3 | 8 |
| 8 | 256 |

   (c) File size = W × H × colour depth = 2000 × 3000 × 24 = 144 000 000 bits
   = 144 000 000/8 bytes = 18 000 000 bytes = 18 megabytes

   (d) Metadata is extra, non-pixel information about the image stored within the file. It can include items such as date and time, the make of camera and camera settings and even the location where it was taken.

## 81. Sound

1   (a) (i)   The frequency at which samples of the analogue sound wave are taken. It is measured in samples per second or Hz (hertz) and kHz (kilohertz).

   (ii)  A high sampling frequency gives a more accurate reproduction of the analogue waveform because the wave is sampled at more points. The file size will increase.

   (b) Bit rate is the amount of data processed every second.
   bit rate = sampling frequency × bit depth

   (c) (i)   bit rate = sampling frequency × bit depth = 50 000 × 16 = 800 000 bits per second

   (ii)  file size = sampling frequency × bit depth × time (seconds) = 44 100 x 100 x 16 bits = 70560000 bits
   = 8820000 bytes = 8.82 megabytes

## 82. Compression

1  (a) Any two of the following:
   - It uses less internet bandwidth when they are sent and received.
   - The transfer speed is quicker.
   - The files take up less storage space on their computers.

   (b) Lossless compression reduces file sizes without deleting any data. When the file is decompressed, it is exactly the same as the original. Nothing is lost. Lossless compression looks for redundancy, where the same data is stored many times, and groups this data into one reference in the file.

   Lossy compression reduces the file size by deleting some data. The original can never be reconstituted when it is decompressed as it has been irreversibly changed.

   (c) PDF file: lossless.

   The novel would be impossible to read if some of the data (words) were removed permanently.

   Images of her trip to London: lossy.

   Areas with very similar colours are merged into one to reduce file size. People cannot distinguish these small differences and so are not aware that the data has been removed.

## PRACTICE

## Computational thinking, algorithms and programming

1  (a) (i)   100100101
      (ii)  Overflow error.
   (b) $128 + 32 + 16 + 8 + 2 + 1 = 187$
   (c) (i)   F7
      (ii)  There are 4 bits for each hexadecimal digit and so it is easy to convert.
            There are fewer digits and so it is easier to remember the code for a particular colour.
   (d) The CPU of a computer contains billions of transistors acting as switches and they are either on or off.
       These two states (off or on) can be represented by the two digits of the binary system: 0 and 1.

2  (a) (i)   Pixels.
      (ii)  The colour depth states the number of bits used to represent the colour value of each pixel.
            The more bits that are used, the greater number of colours that can be represented.
      (iii) File size = $5000 \times 4000 \times 24$ bits = $480\,000\,000$ bits
            = $60\,000\,000$ bytes
            = 60 megabytes
   (b) The resolution of the image has been lowered as the same number of pixels are now spread over a greater area and the size of each pixel has been increased. This reduces the clarity and sharpness of the image.
   (c) (i)   Metadata.
      (ii)  Any two from:
            name of camera, type of lens used, camera settings, location where image was taken.
   (d) (i)   The file size is reduced by permanently removing some of the information, so when the file is decompressed it is not the same as the original.
      (ii)  Areas with very similar colours are merged into one to reduce file size. People cannot distinguish these small differences and so do not realise that the data has been removed. With text files, letters and words would be permanently deleted and the text would not make sense.

3  (a) An array allows multiple items of the same data type to be stored under one identifier or name.
       The array means that Stephen does not have to use multiple variables.

   (b)

| Laos | Cambodia | India | Australia | Nepal | Peru |
|------|----------|-------|-----------|-------|------|
| Cambodia | India | Australia | Laos | Nepal | Peru |
| Cambodia | Australia | India | Laos | Nepal | Peru |
| Australia | Cambodia | India | Laos | Nepal | Peru |

   (c)
```
found = False
index = 0
country = input("Please enter a country.")
while found == False OR index <= countries.
length - 1
   if countries[index] = country then
      found = True
   endif
   index = index + 1
endwhile
if found = True then
   print(country + " is in the list.")
else
   print(country + " is not in the list.")
endif
```
   (d)
```
myFile = openWrite("Countries.txt")
for index = 0 to countries.length - 1
   myFile.writeLine(countries[index])
next index
myfile.close()
```

**4** (a) 00111010

(b) 01010100

(c) 00011001

**5** (a)

| A | B | Q |
|---|---|---|
| 0 | 0 | 0 |
| 0 | 1 | 0 |
| 1 | 0 | 1 |
| 1 | 1 | 0 |

(b)

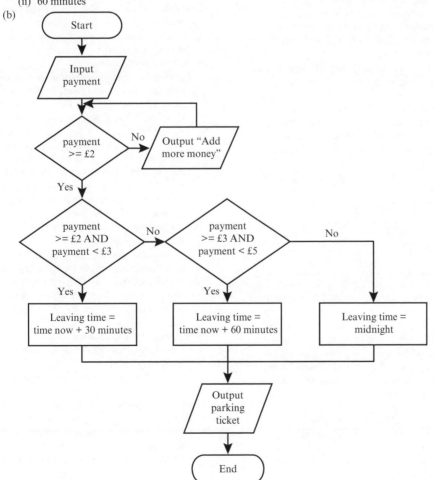

| A | B | P |
|---|---|---|
| 0 | 0 | 1 |
| 0 | 1 | 0 |
| 1 | 0 | 0 |
| 1 | 1 | 0 |

**6** (a) Source code editor – autocompletes words as they are typed OR bracket matching OR auto indentation OR colour coding of key words.

Debugger to identify errors in the code – single stepping OR breakpoints OR variable tracing.

(b) choice – character OR string

conversion – real

(c) This is one possible solution. There are other possible solutions.

```
acceptable = False
while acceptable == False
    choice = input("Which units are you entering? Enter 'I' for inches and 'C' for centimetres.")
    if choice == "I" OR choice == "C" then
        acceptable = True
    else
        print("Sorry that is not recognised.")
    endif
endwhile
```

**7** (a) (i)  £2

(ii)  60 minutes

(b)

8 (a) (i) ProductID
    (ii) This field contains the only data that is unique to each record.
(b) 4
(c) SELECT * FROM Products
    WHERE Supplier LIKE "Smith and Co";
(d) SELECT Name, Supplier, ReorderLevel
    FROM Products
    WHERE ReorderLevel < 50 AND Supplier LIKE "Jacob's";

## Computer systems

1 (a)

| Component | Function |
|---|---|
| CU (Control Unit) | The CU controls the other components of the CPU and coordinates the fetch–execute cycle. |
| Program counter | The program counter holds the address in RAM of the next instruction to be taken to the CPU. |
| MAR (Memory Address Register) | The MAR holds the address of the memory location currently being read from or written to. |
| MDR (Memory Data Register) | The MDR is a temporary store (buffer) for anything copied from memory. |
| ALU (Arithmetic Logic Unit) | The ALU performs arithmetic and logical operations to carry out program instructions. |

(b) In parallel processing, the cores work together on the same program. This is faster than having a single core working on the program.
In multitasking, the cores can work on different programs at the same time, which improves productivity by performing several tasks simultaneously.
(c) Frequently used instructions are stored in the cache memory, which is far faster than the memory used in RAM. Instructions in the cache are fetched more quickly than instructions fetched from RAM, which improves performance.
(d) Virtual memory is an area of the hard disk drive or solid state drive used as temporary RAM when the actual RAM is full. The least recently used data is swapped out to the swap file when the RAM is full so that new instructions that need to be executed can be moved to the RAM. When the instructions in the virtual memory are required, they need to be swapped back into the RAM. This lowers performance.
(e)

| | RAM | ROM |
|---|---|---|
| Program instructions and data are stored here. | ✓ | |
| It is used to boot up the laptop when it is switched on. | | ✓ |
| It is volatile. | ✓ | |

2 (a) Machine code is the language that the processor directly understands. It can process instructions when presented as 1s and 0s.
(b) High-level languages are similar to human languages. They provide built-in data structures and constructs such as selection and iteration. They have libraries of functions that programmers can use instead of having to write them all themselves. High-level languages cannot be understood by processors.
(c) Any two of the following:
• The program can be written more quickly as programmers are using a language more like their own natural language.
• There will be fewer errors in the code as programmers are using a familiar language.

• Programmers will not have to write completely new code for each device on which the game is to be played.
• High-level languages can be portable and can be translated for different machines whereas machine code is specific to a particular machine.

3 (a) To provide long-term permanent storage for files and data. These files and data cannot be stored permanently in RAM because they would be lost when a computer is switched off as RAM is volatile.
(b)

| Situation | Magnetic, optical or solid state | Reason why this is the most appropriate |
|---|---|---|
| Storing images, videos and music in a hand held device. | Solid state | Fast access time, therefore many images can be taken. No moving parts so it is very portable and robust. |
| Data storage in the file servers of a large network. | Magnetic | Magnetic drives have a very large capacity. Fast data access times and cheaper per Gb of storage than solid state. No need to worry about robustness since the file servers don't get moved around. |
| Storing programs, images and videos to be given away free with a computer magazine. | Optical | Cheap, light and portable. Most computers have a CD or DVD player to access the data on them. |

4 (a) Malware is software that has been designed to gain unauthorised access to a computer system in order to disrupt its functioning or to collect information without the user's knowledge.
(b) Any two of the following:
• A **virus** is a computer program hidden inside another program. Viruses can delete or corrupt data held on an infected computer. A virus can replicate itself and insert itself into other programs or files which can be passed on.
• A **worm** does not need another program to carry it. It can replicate and send itself in emails, which are then sent to everyone in a user's address book. Worms consume computer resources as they are reproducing and they allow criminals to gain access to the infected computer and take it over.
• **Trojans** are installed by users when they think they are installing legitimate software.
Trojans can delete files, change the desktop layout and send screenshots and key presses to the hacker's computer.
• **Spyware** often comes packaged with other software and the user does not know they are installing it. It spies on the user like a Trojan by sending information to a criminal.
(c) Any two of the following:
• Install antivirus software and ensure that it is constantly updated.
• Ensure that the antivirus software can scan emails.
• Use adware removal software.
• Install anti-spyware software that removes or blocks spyware.
• Avoid opening emails and attachments from unknown sources.
• Ensure that the operating system is up to date.
• Install the latest security updates.

**5** (a)

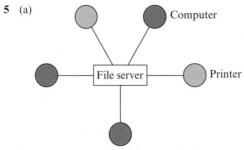

Computer

File server

Printer

(b) Any two points from the following list:
- The server is responsible for network security by allocating login names and passwords to users.
- The server can allocate the access rights of the users.
- The server stores all of the programs and files for the users.
- The server can centrally back up all data that is stored.
- The server handles requests for data/services from clients.

(c) A protocol is a set of rules for transmission of data over a network so that the data can be understood by the sending and receiving computers.

(d) (i)

| Layer | Order |
|---|---|
| Transport layer | 2 |
| Network access layer | 4 |
| Application layer | 1 |
| Internet layer | 3 |

(ii) Any two points from the following list:
- The overall model is simplified by dividing it into its functional parts.
- Different layers can be combined in different ways as required.
- One layer can be developed or changed without affecting the other layers.
- Allocating specific tasks makes it easier to identify and correct networking errors and problems.
- It provides a universal standard for hardware and software manufacturers to follow so that their devices will be able to communicate with each other.

(e) The answer should include as many of the following points as possible. You would not be expected to give all the points for the full 8 marks awarded for the question.

**Penetration testing**

The company should employ a security expert to carry out penetration testing of its network so as to identify vulnerabilities and recommend ways of making the network more secure.

**Network forensics**

The company should use network forensics to monitor, record and analyse network events such as who has logged in, how many unsuccessful attempts have been made and what users have done.

Network forensics can identify unusual network activity. The analysis can be used as legal evidence if illegal activity is detected.

**Authentication**

Passwords should be:
- strong – at least 8 characters and include non-alphanumeric characters, e.g. ! or ?, and be changed regularly
- never written down or shared.

Old passwords should never be reused.

**User access levels** are used to set which files and folders users are allowed to:
- see and browse
- edit or delete.

**Network policies** are rules which should set out:
- what users can and cannot do on the network, e.g. must not use removable storage devices, install their own software or download files from internet sites
- when backups will be made and where they will be kept
- what should be done if there is a problem or breach of security.

**Anti-malware software**
- This software is designed to detect and remove malware, e.g. antivirus or spyware removal software.
- Anti-malware software should be constantly updated to tackle new threats.
- Operating systems should be kept up to date as new security features are introduced.

**Encryption**
- Encryption is the conversion of data into a form that cannot be understood unless a user knows how to convert it back again.
- These conversions are called encrypting and decrypting the data, and keys are required. Hackers of the network would not have the required keys.

**Firewalls**
- A firewall protects a network connected to a WAN such as the internet.
- It can be provided by hardware or software.
- Firewalls can be configured to prevent communications from entering the network and also to prevent programs and users from accessing the internet from within the network.

**6** (a) B    (b) C    (c) A    (d) C

**7** (a) Proprietary software is commercially produced by an organisation for a profit and must be paid for.
Open-source software is free to use and users can modify the source code.

(b) For example:
- The software is developed professionally and carefully tested, so the students should not have problems using it.
- Support will be provided to keep customers happy so that they will keep using the software.
- There will be books, magazine articles and online tutorials for the students to use.
- Users cannot access the source code and the licence agreement restricts what they are allowed to do with it, i.e. the number of computer the software can be installed on.

(c) Any two points from the following list:
- It is free to download and use.
- All the students will be able to use the same software at home as they are using at school.
- The school can modify the source code to adapt it to their needs.

# Notes

# Notes

# Notes

# Notes

# Notes

# Notes

Published by Pearson Education Limited, 80 Strand, London, WC2R 0RL.

www.pearsonschoolsandfecolleges.co.uk

Text and illustrations © Pearson 2017

Typeset, illustrated and produced by Tech-Set Ltd, Gateshead
Cover illustration by Miriam Sturdee

The right of David Waller to be identified as author of this work has been asserted by him in accordance with the Copyright, Designs and Patents Act 1988.

First published 2017

20  19  18 17
10 9 8 7 6 5 4 3 2

**British Library Cataloguing in Publication Data**
A catalogue record for this book is available from the British Library

ISBN 978 1 292 13389 8

Printed in Slovakia by Neografia

**Acknowledgements**
The publisher would like to thank the following for their kind permission to reproduce their photographs:

(Key: b-bottom; c-centre; l-left; r-right; t-top)

**Alamy Stock Photo:** J Marshall - Tribaleye Images 84t, 84b; **Shutterstock.com:** Iakov Kalinin 80

All other images © Pearson Education

**Note from the publisher**

Pearson has robust editorial processes, including answer and fact checks, to ensure the accuracy of the content in this publication, and every effort is made to ensure this publication is free of errors. We are, however, only human, and occasionally errors do occur. Pearson is not liable for any misunderstandings that arise as a result of errors in this publication, but it is our priority to ensure that the content is accurate. If you spot an error, please do contact us at resourcescorrections@pearson.com so we can make sure it is corrected.